BOOK 4
PATTERNS IN SPELLING
Patterns with Other Vowel Sounds and Spellings

TIM BROWN

DEBORAH F. KNIGHT

NEW READERS PRESS
Publishing Division of Laubach Literacy International
Syracuse, New York

About the Authors

Deborah Knight began her teaching career in the early 1970s and has taught both reading and English in urban, suburban, and rural settings. Since 1984, Ms. Knight has served as the Coordinator of the Learning Disabilities Assistance Program at Onondaga Community College in Syracuse, New York. Working closely with these OCC students, she has helped them to develop strategies for improving their reading, writing, spelling, and study skills.

Tim Brown has worked with developing and remedial readers and writers since 1978. He teaches courses in spelling as well as freshman composition and literature at Onondaga Community College. He also serves as Senior Professional Tutor at the college's Writing Skills Center, where he has a special interest in teaching spelling to developing and remedial writers and ESL students.

ON THE COVER: A quilt entitled *Rhythm/Color: Morris Men*; 99½″ x 99½″, by Michael James. This work of art appeared in *The Art Quilt* exhibit and book of the same name. It is reproduced here through the courtesy of The Quilt Digest Press.

ISBN 0-88336-106-X

© 1990

New Readers Press
Publishing Division of Laubach Literacy International
Box 131, Syracuse, New York 13210

Printed in the United States of America

Project Editor: Christina M. Jagger
Manuscript Editor: Mary Hutchison
Designed by Chris Steenwerth
Cover by Chris Steenwerth
Illustrations by Christine Patsos-Kocak
Composition by Anne Hyde
Layout Artist: Joanne Groth

9 8 7 6 5 4 3

Table of Contents

Lesson 1

The Word Families *ude*, *use*, *uce*, and *ule*

Continents		
Continents		
Asia	North America	Europe
Africa	South America	Australia
		Antarctica

Word Families

ude

① Listening

Listen to the sound of *ude* in these words.

rude	delude	denude	attitude
crude	include	prelude	gratitude
intrude	seclude	solitude	latitude
protrude	conclude	aptitude	longitude

use

Listen to the sound of *use* in these words.

use	fuse	abuse	accuse
misuse	refuse	diffuse	excuse
useful	confuse	profuse	amusement

uce

Listen to the sound of *uce* in these words.

truce	reduce	produce	introduce
spruce	deduce	reproduce	inducement

ule

Listen to the sound of *ule* in these words.

rule	mule	capsule	molecule
ruler	yule	ridicule	schedule

2 Writing Words. On the lines below, write the words that you hear.

1. _____   5. _____   9. _____
2. _____   6. _____   10. _____
3. _____   7. _____   11. _____
4. _____   8. _____   12. _____

3 Dictionary Skills: Alphabetizing. On the lines below, alphabetize the words you wrote in Exercise 2.

1. _____   5. _____   9. _____
2. _____   6. _____   10. _____
3. _____   7. _____   11. _____
4. _____   8. _____   12. _____

4 Completing Sentences. Fill in each blank in the sentences below with the name of one of the continents of the earth. Consult a map, atlas, or other reference if necessary. The names may be used more than once.

1. France, Italy, Spain, and Germany are in _____.

2. The United States and Canada are in _____.

3. Egypt, Kenya, and Nigeria are in _____.

4. Brazil, Colombia, and Argentina are in _____.

5. China, India, and Vietnam are in _____.

6. _____ is almost entirely covered with ice and snow.

7. A country that is also a continent is _____.

8. The continent where I was born is _____.

9. A continent where some of my ancestors lived is _____.

10. A continent that I would like to visit is _____.

5 **Review of Silent _e_ Pattern 1.** The silent _e_ at the end of a word is dropped when an ending that starts with a vowel is added. When the ending starts with a consonant, the silent _e_ is not dropped. Add the endings to the words below.

1. rude + ly _____

2. refuse + al _____

3. reduce + ing _____

4. produce + er _____

5. abuse + ive _____

6. schedule + ed _____

7. include + ing _____

8. intrude + er _____

9. crude + ly _____

10. introduce + ing _____

6 **Word Building.** Some words in the _use_ family are sometimes pronounced like _uce_ family words. Fill in the missing letters in the sentences below with either _use_ or _uce_.

1. What exc___ ___ ___ did Bert give for not finishing the job?

2. Our neighbors have three large spr___ ___ ___ trees in their back yard.

3. Rashid will see that these tools are put to good ___ ___ ___.

4. That car has taken a lot of ab___ ___ ___.

5. Gretchen will introd___ ___ ___ the speaker at the next meeting.

7 **Syllable Types.** The five types of syllables you have studied are listed below. An example of each type is given. Write another example of each type of syllable on the lines provided.

Syllable Type	Example	Your Example
1. Closed	mop	_____
2. Open	re	_____
3. Cle	ble	_____
4. VCe	ude	_____
5. Double Vowel	ain	_____

8 **Writing Words by Syllables.** Write each word your teacher dictates by syllables. Then write the entire word on the line provided.

First Syllable	Second Syllable	Third Syllable	Fourth Syllable	Whole Word
1. _____	_____			_____
2. _____	_____			_____
3. _____	_____	_____		_____
4. _____	_____	_____		_____
5. _____	_____			_____
6. _____	_____	_____		_____
7. _____	_____	_____	_____	_____

Use three of the words above in original sentences.

_____

_____

_____

9 **Writing Sentences.** On the lines below, write the sentences that you hear.

1. _____

2. _____

3. _____

4. _____

5. _____

_____

6. _____

_____

Lesson 2

The Word Families *ute, ume, une,* and *uke*

Capital Cities		
London	Moscow	Tokyo
Mexico City	Ottawa	Washington, D.C.

Word Families

ute

ume

une

uke

❶ Listening

Listen to the sound of *ute* in these words.

mute	dispute	flute	astute
cute	commute	dilute	absolute
execute	computer	salute	parachute
prosecute	distribute	pollute	substitute

Listen to the sound of *ume* in these words.

fume	assume	legume
plume	resume	costume
perfume	presume	consumer

Listen to the sound of *une* in these words.

June	dune	attuned	immune
tune	prune	opportune	communed

Listen to the sound of *uke* in these words.

duke	Luke	fluke	rebuke

❷ Writing Words. On the lines below, write the words that you hear.

1. _____   4. _____   7. _____

2. _____   5. _____   8. _____

3. _____   6. _____   9. _____

3 **Dictionary Skills: Alphabetizing.** On the lines below, alphabetize the words you wrote in Exercise 2.

1. _____   4. _____   7. _____

2. _____   5. _____   8. _____

3. _____   6. _____   9. _____

4 **Completing Sentences.** Fill in each blank in the sentences below with the name of a capital city. Use an atlas or dictionary if necessary.

1. The capital of the United States of America is _____.

2. The capital of Mexico is _____.

3. The capital of Japan is _____.

4. The capital of Canada is _____.

5. The capital of England is _____.

6. The capital of the Union of Soviet Socialist Republics is _____.

7. The capital of your state or province is _____.

8. A capital city you would like to visit is _____.

5 **Word Building.** Write the missing syllable of each word you hear.

1. com put _____   4. pros e _____ tor   7. _____ lu mine

2. con _____ er   5. dis _____   8. for _____ nate

3. im _____ nize   6. com _____ er   9. op _____ tu ni ty

Use two of these words in original sentences.

_____

_____

6 **More Word Building.** Add one of the word families listed below to each of the consonants or blends to make a word. Do not make the same word twice.

ude	use	uce	ule
ute	ume	une	uke

1. c_____   5. f_____   9. r_____

2. cr_____   6. m_____   10. r_____

3. d_____   7. m_____   11. t_____

4. d_____   8. pl_____   12. tr_____

7 **Review of Silent *e* Pattern 1.** Add the endings to the words below following Silent *e* Pattern 1.

1. consume + er _____   6. pollute + ing _____

2. confuse + ing _____   7. pollute + ion _____

3. confuse + ion _____   8. prosecute + or _____

4. constitute + ed _____   9. prosecute + ed _____

5. constitute + ion _____   10. prosecute + ion _____

8 **Review of the Endings -*tion* and -*sion*.** The endings -*tion* and -*sion* are added to verbs to form nouns. Sometimes when these endings are added, the root word changes or some other letters are added, but you can usually hear the changes. Add either -*tion* or -*sion* to the words below. Look the words up in your dictionary when you need to.

1. introduce _____   7. accuse _____

2. produce _____   8. salute _____

3. reduce _____   9. compute _____

4. conclude _____   10. resume _____

5. include _____   11. assume _____

6. intrude _____   12. presume _____

9 **Writing Addresses.** Address the envelope using names you choose from the lists below. Use your own name and address for the return address in the upper left-hand corner.

First Names	Last Names	Streets	Cities/States/ZIP Codes
Bruce	Gruber	1001 Hubert Street	Butte, MT 59701
June	Kucinski	785 Julian Avenue	Duluth, MN 55802
Julio	Luciano	422 Nugent Road	Juneau, AK 99803
Luke	Cruz	1716 Rudolph Boulevard	Syracuse, NY 13204
Trudy	Rubenstein	39 Trusdell Court	Tucson, AZ 85705

Name _____

Street _____

City   State   ZIP

Name _____

Street _____

City   State   ZIP

10 **Writing Sentences.** On the lines below, write the sentences that you hear.

1. _____

2. _____

3. _____

4. _____

5. _____

   _____

Lesson 3

The Word Families *u*, *ue*, *ew*, and *o*

Sight Words			
ewe	neuter	maneuver	recruit
feud	neutral	nuisance	pursuit

Word Families

1 Listening

u

Listen to the sound of *u* in these words.

flu	ruby	menu	fuel
fluent	ruin	human	unit
duty	rumor	humor	union
truly	super	future	universe

ue

Listen to the sound of *ue* in these words.

sue	due	issue	argue
true	subdue	pursue	value
clue	residue	statue	rescue
glue	Tuesday	gruesome	continue

ew

Listen to the sound of *ew* in these words.

blew	flew	new	few
chew	grew	renew	curfew
drew	Jewish	steward	nephew

o

Listen to the sound of *o* in these words.

ado	whom	prove	move
into	tomb	improve	remover
unto	womb	approval	movement

2 Writing Words. On the lines below, write the words that you hear.

1. _____   5. _____   9. _____

2. _____   6. _____   10. _____

3. _____   7. _____   11. _____

4. _____   8. _____   12. _____

3 Using Sight Words. Each of the sight words in this lesson has an unusual spelling for long *u*. Underline the letters that spell long *u* in each of the words below.

ewe	neuter	maneuver	recruit
feud	neutral	nuisance	pursuit

Fill in the blanks in the sentences below with one of these sight words. Use each word only once.

1. That puppy is beginning to be a _____.

2. The word *it* is a _____ pronoun.

3. How many lambs has that _____ had?

4. Rudy didn't take sides in the argument; he remained _____.

5. The new _____ is going through basic training now.

6. The Hatfields and the McCoys had a long and famous _____.

7. Can you _____ the car into that small parking space?

8. The Declaration of Independence says that among our unalienable rights are "life, liberty, and the _____ of happiness."

Choose two of the sight words and use them in original sentences.

_____

_____

4 **Discovering a Pattern.** Underline *ue* or *ew* in the words below and answer the questions that follow.

subdue	due.	pursue	few	pew	nephew
argue	true	rescue	chew	grew	renew

1. Where are the underlined letters in each word? _____

   Pattern: The long *u* spellings *ue* and *ew* will usually be found at the _____ of words or syllables.

2. What representative word in the *ue* family does not follow this pattern?

   _____

5 **Review of Silent *e* Pattern 1**

Part A. Add the endings to the words below. Drop the final silent *e* when necessary.

1. unite + ed _____   7. continue + ing _____

2. subdue + ed _____   8. universe + al _____

3. value + able _____   9. improve + ment _____

4. move + ment _____   10. rescue + ed _____

5. prove + able _____   11. residue + al _____

6. remove + al _____   12. pursue + ing _____

Part B. Answer the questions below to discover two exceptions to Silent *e* Pattern 1.

1. Write the root words of *truly* and *argument*. _____ and _____

2. What letter does each root word end in? _____

3. Do the suffixes *-ly* and *-ment* begin with consonants or vowels? _____

4. What happens to the silent *e*'s in *true* and *argue* when the suffixes *-ly* and *-ment* are

   added? _____

6 **Dictionary Skills: Homonyms.** The long *u* families have some homonyms that can be confused. To determine the correct spelling, you must know the meaning of the word in context. A dictionary can help you choose the correct word. Answer the following questions, using a dictionary when necessary.

1. Are the bills *dew*, *do*, or *due*? _____

2. Was Jane sick with the *flew* or the *flu*? _____

3. Is the color of the sky *blew* or *blue*? _____

4. Is a type of evergreen a *ewe*, a *yew*, or a *you*? _____

5. Is a recent purchase *knew* or *new*? _____

6. Does a chimney have a *flu* or a *flue*? _____

7 **Alternative Spellings for Long *u*.** Long *u* can be spelled several ways, including *o* and *u*. If the words or phrases your teacher dictates have the spelling *o* for long *u*, write them in the **o** column. Write them in the **u** column if they spell long *u* with a *u*.

o	**u**
_____	_____
_____	_____
_____	_____
_____	_____

8 **Writing Sentences.** On the lines below, write the sentences that you hear.

1. _____

2. _____

3. _____

4. _____

5. _____

_____

Lesson 4

The Word Families *oo*, *oon*, *oom*, *ool*, and *oof*

Sight Words		
cuckoo	wash	guy
muscle	water	geyser

Word Families

1 Listening

oo

Listen to the sound of *oo* in these words.

too	bamboo	food	taboo
woo	tattoo	moody	boost
zoo	shampoo	noodle	rooster

oon

Listen to the sound of *oon* in these words.

soon	cocoon	afternoon	maroon
moon	balloon	honeymoon	racoon
noon	cartoon	tablespoon	typhoon

oom

Listen to the sound of *oom* in these words.

room	bloom	zoom	classroom
doom	gloom	heirloom	storeroom
boom	broomstick	mushroom	courtroom

ool

Listen to the sound of *ool* in these words.

cool	spool	fool	footstool
tool	school	foolish	whirlpool

oof

Listen to the sound of *oof* in these words.

roof	aloof	fireproof
proof	spoof	foolproof

2 **Writing Words.** On the lines below, write the words that you hear.

1. _____   5. _____   9. _____

2. _____   6. _____   10. _____

3. _____   7. _____   11. _____

4. _____   8. _____   12. _____

3 **Words Ending in Long _u_.** You have studied five ways to spell long _u_ at the end of words: _u_, _ue_, _ew_, _o_, and _oo_. Write the words that you hear under the correct headings below.

ue	ew	oo
1. _____	1. _____	1. _____
2. _____	2. _____	2. _____
3. _____	3. _____	3. _____
4. _____	4. _____	4. _____

u	o
1. _____	1. _____
2. _____	2. _____

4 **Word Building.** Add one of the word families below to each of the consonants or blends to make a word. Do not make the same word twice.

_oo_   _oon_   _oom_   _ool_   _oof_

1. b_____   5. pr_____   9. st_____

2. c_____   6. r_____   10. t_____

3. m_____   7. r_____   11. t_____

4. n_____   8. sp_____   12. z_____

5 **Word Building: Compound Words.** Form compound words by adding one of the *oo* words below to the beginning or end of each of the words listed. Check your dictionary to see if your compounds are closed, hyphenated, or open.

moon   *noon*   *proof*   *room*   *spoon*

1. bed _____
2. tea _____
3. time _____
4. work _____
5. sound _____

6. light _____
7. mate _____
8. water _____
9. beam _____
10. read _____

6 **Alternative Spellings for Long *u*.** Long *u* is commonly spelled uCe and ooC. If the words or phrases your teacher dictates contain the uCe pattern, write them in the **uCe** column. Write them in the **ooC** column if they contain the ooC pattern.

uCe	**ooC**
_____	_____
_____	_____
_____	_____
_____	_____

7 **Reviewing Contractions.** A contraction is formed by combining two words, leaving out one or more letters. An apostrophe (′) is used in place of the omitted letter or letters. Write the contractions for the words below.

1. she will _____
2. would not _____
3. I am _____
4. they are _____
5. it is _____

6. have not _____
7. you are _____
8. he would _____
9. we are _____
10. is not _____

8 **Writing Sentences.** On the lines below, write the sentences that you hear.

1. _____
2. _____
3. _____
4. _____
5. _____

9 **Composing Sentences.** On a separate piece of paper, write three or four sentences about this scene. Use some of the long *u* words listed below.

afternoon	continue	future	produce	Tuesday
aptitude	distribute	improve	pursue	value
classroom	due	June	schedule	use
computer	fluent	new	school	useful

Lesson 5

The Word Families *oop*, *oot*, *oose*, *ooth*, and *ou*

Sight Words

bouquet	bouillon	troupe
soufflé		souvenir

Word Families

1 Listening

oop

Listen to the sound of *oop* in these words.

coop	scoop	droop	snoop
hoop	stoop	troop	loophole

oot

Listen to the sound of *oot* in these words.

boot	hoot	shoot	uproot
loot	root	scooter	offshoot

oose

Listen to the sound of *oose* in these words.

goose	loose	noose	choose
moose	loosen	caboose	

ooth

Listen to the sound of *ooth* in these words.

booth	toothache	smooth
tooth	toothbrush	soothing

ou

Listen to the sound of *ou* in these words.

you	soup	route	rouge
youth	croup	routine	coupon

2 Writing Words. On the lines below, write the words that you hear.

1. _____   4. _____   7. _____

2. _____   5. _____   8. _____

3. _____   6. _____   9. _____

3 Dictionary Skills: Word Origins. Words have come into English from many different languages. Sometimes knowing what language a word comes from can help you remember how to spell it. Many dictionaries list the origins of root words. Look up these words and write the language from which each came on the line beside it. Underline the letters that spell long *u* in each word. Then complete the pattern below.

1. bouillon _____   5. soup _____

2. bouquet _____   6. souvenir _____

3. coupon _____   7. troupe _____

4. route _____   8. trousseau _____

Pattern: Long *u* is often spelled _____ in words taken from

_____.

4 Word Building. You have studied several ways to spell long *u*, including *u, ue, ew, o, oo,* and *ou.* Fill in the correct spelling of long *u* to complete each word below. Then write the entire word on the line provided.

1. contin_____ _____   8. ball_____n _____

2. sp_____n _____   9. pr_____ve _____

3. purs_____ _____   10. incl_____de _____

4. prod_____ce _____   11. neph_____ _____

5. r_____tine _____   12. am_____se _____

6. bl_____m _____   13. T_____sday _____

7. fl_____id _____   14. gr_____p _____

5 **Proofreading.** It is sometimes hard to know which spelling to use when you hear the long *u* sound. Each of the words below is spelled two ways. Underline the one that you think is correct. Then look up the word in your dictionary to be sure you are right. When you have checked the spelling, write the word on the line provided. If some of these spellings look strange to you, congratulations. Your memory of what a word looks like is working well.

1. soop   soup   _____

2. routine   rootine   _____

3. ruster   rooster   _____

4. saloot   salute   _____

5. tissue   tissoo   _____

6 **Homonym Review:** *To, Too,* **or** *Two*. Fill in the blanks in the sentences below with *to, too,* or *two.*

1. Luke has _____ daughters.

2. Are you confused, _____?

3. I want _____ read this book.

4. The Carsons are going to be there, _____.

5. The group voted _____ add _____ members.

6. There are _____ many people at this amusement park.

7 **Dictionary Skills: More Homonyms.** Answer the following questions, using a dictionary when necessary.

1. Does a tree have *roots* or *routes*?   _____

2. Is the new growth from a seed a *chute* or a *shoot*?   _____

3. Is a female sheep a *ewe* or a *you*?   _____

4. Is a group of performers a *troop* or a *troupe*?   _____

5. Would you play on the strings of a *loot* or a *lute*?   _____

8 **Reviewing Patterns for Adding Endings.** Review these patterns for adding endings and then add the endings to the words below.

1. **Doubling Pattern 1.** Double the final consonant if the word has one syllable, one vowel, and one final consonant, and the ending begins with a vowel. Do not double *w* or *x*.

2. **Doubling Pattern 2.** When adding an ending that starts with a vowel to words with more than one syllable, double the final consonant only when the accent falls on the last syllable and the last syllable has one vowel and one final consonant. Do not double *w* or *x*.

3. **Silent *e* Pattern 1.** Drop the final silent *e* if the ending begins with a vowel.

4. **Silent *e* Pattern 2.** Do not drop the final silent *e* from a word that ends in *ce* or *ge* if the ending begins with *a* or *o*.

5. **Changing *y* to *i*.** When adding an ending to a word that ends in **C***y*, change the *y* to *i* unless the ending begins with *i*. Add *-es* instead of *-s* to nouns and verbs.

6. **Changing *f* to *v*.** The plural of some words that end in *f* or *fe* is formed by changing the *f* to *v* and adding *-es*.

1. glue + ing _____   5. forgot + en _____

2. duty + s *or* es _____   6. chew + ed _____

3. stop + ing _____   7. schedule + ing _____

4. hoof + s *or* es _____   8. outrage + ous _____

Use one of the words you formed in an original sentence.

_____

_____

9 **Writing Sentences.** On the lines below, write the sentences that you hear.

1. _____

2. _____

3. _____

4. _____

5. _____

Review of Unit 1

The Long *u*

1 **Writing Words That End in Long *u*.** Write each word you hear under the correct heading.

ue	ew	oo
_____	_____	_____
_____	_____	_____
_____	_____	_____

u	o
_____	_____
_____	_____

2 **Word Building.** Fill in the blanks in the words below with *u, ue, ew, o, oo,* or *ou* to correctly spell the long *u* sound.

1. Some mushr_____ms can be eaten, but toadst_____ls are usually poisonous.

2. There is a very h_____morous cart_____n in the aftern_____n n_____spaper.

3. On T_____sday, we'll contin_____ the gr_____p discussions we started t_____day.

4. If y_____ buy that t_____thpaste, I have a c_____pon y_____ can _____se.

5. Ruby bought perf_____me, shamp_____, and nail polish rem_____ver at the store.

6. Julie's neph._____ resc_____d a bird that fl_____ int_____ their picture window.

7. The waitress rem_____ved the f_____d from the table and brought the dessert men_____.

8. I ass_____me that comp_____ters will be _____seful t_____ls in the f_____ture.

3 **More Word Building.** Add a word part from Column 2 to each word part in Column 1 to make a word. Write the words on the lines provided. Use each word part in Column 1 only once.

Column 1   **Column 2**

a	due	1. _____	6. _____
bal	ew		
men	ler	2. _____	7. _____
neph	loon		
pur	muse	3. _____	8. _____
rou	pid		
ru	poo	4. _____	9. _____
sham	sue		
stu	tine	5. _____	10. _____
sub	u		

4 **Review of Silent _e_ Pattern 1.** Add the suffixes and prefixes to the root words. Remember to drop the final silent _e_ when necessary.

1. pollute + ed   _____

2. argue + ed   _____

3. protrude + ing _____

4. loose + ly   _____

5. move + ing   _____

6. confuse + ion   _____

7. re + move + er _____

8. issue + ed   _____

9. pursue + ing   _____

10. consume + er   _____

11. in + value + able   _____

12. im + move + able   _____

13. conclude + ing   _____

14. accumulate + ion _____

15. prosecute + ion   _____

16. constitute + ion   _____

17. im + prove + ment _____

18. dis + approve + al _____

19. ridicule + ous   _____

20. de + nude + ing   _____

Now form the words below that are exceptions to Silent _e_ Pattern 1.

1. true + ly   _____   2. argue + ment _____

5 **Writing Words by Syllables.** Write the words your teacher dictates by syllables. Then write the entire word on the line provided.

	First Syllable	Second Syllable	Third Syllable	Fourth Syllable		Whole Word
1.	_____	_____				_____
2.	_____	_____				_____
3.	_____	_____	_____			_____
4.	_____	_____	_____			_____
5.	_____	_____	_____			_____
6.	_____	_____	_____	_____		_____
7.	_____	_____	_____	_____		_____
8.	_____	_____	_____	_____		_____

Use three of the words you wrote in original sentences.

_____

_____

_____

6 **Reviewing Contractions.** Write the contractions for the pairs of words below.

1. I would _____
2. has not _____
3. you will _____
4. he had _____
5. will not _____
6. we have _____

7. had not _____
8. are not _____
9. she has _____
10. could not _____
11. do not _____
12. should have _____

7 **Proofreading.** It is sometimes hard to know which spelling to use when you hear the long *u* sound. Each of the words below is spelled two ways. Underline the one that you think is correct. Then look up the word in your dictionary to be sure you are right. When you have checked the spelling, write the word on the line provided.

1. rootine   routine   _____

2. truly   truley   _____

3. inclood   include   _____

4. choose   chuse   _____

5. Tuseday   Tuesday   _____

6. roode   rude   _____

7. nephew   nephue   _____

8. move   moove   _____

8 **Homonyms.** Write sentences using each of the homonyms below.

1. flu   _____

2. flew   _____

3. root   _____

4. route   _____

5. do   _____

6. due   _____

7. blew   _____

8. blue   _____

9. knew   _____

10. new   _____

Acknowledgments

For me, second books in a series are always more difficult to write than the first. I think it has something to do with spending so much time with your characters in book one that it's hard to convince yourself that it's okay to move forward. There's quite a list of people who convinced me—and maybe dragged me kicking and screaming—through the process of writing *Not Your Ex's Hexes*.

First off, a huge thank-you to my hubby and kids for embracing eat-out nights and delivery dine-in as well as you did when I was under deadline. I choose to think it was more a show of support and less due to the fact you didn't want me setting off the smoke alarm yet again.

In no particular order, a big shout-out and thank-you to everyone at St. Martin's Press, from marketing to publicity, to the art department (can we say "hey, baby" to the gorgeous cover). Kerry Resnick (designer) and illustrator Carina Lindmeier can do no wrong. For *Not Your Ex's Hexes*, I was blessed to work with two incredible editors, Jennie Conway and the super supportive Tiffany Shelton. Not only did they call me out on my exorbitant amount of em-dashes and ellipses, but they made sure I knew I had support every inch of the way and through every keystroke.

Kristin Dwyer, my publicist . . . lady, you're a rock star. I don't know how you do half of what you do and keep things straight. Hell, I don't know how you can keep ME straight. (If you have a step-by-step process for the latter, my hubby is totally interested in learning your Magic.)

9 **Finding Root Words.** Write the root word of each of the words listed. Then write the number of the pattern below that was followed when the ending was added. Review the patterns in Exercise 8 of Lesson 5 if necessary.

1. Doubling Pattern 1   3. Silent *e* Pattern 1   5. Changing *y* to *i*
2. Doubling Pattern 2   4. Silent *e* Pattern 2   6. Changing *f* to *v*

Word	Root Word	Pattern
1. rescuing	_____	_____
2. dutiful	_____	_____
3. runner	_____	_____
4. courageous	_____	_____
5. beginning	_____	_____
6. hooves	_____	_____
7. inexcusable	_____	_____
8. losing	_____	_____

10 **Writing Sentences.** On the lines below, write the sentences that you hear.

1. _____

2. _____

3. _____

4. _____

5. _____

6. _____

7. _____

8. _____

11 **Crossword Puzzle.** Use the clues below to complete this crossword puzzle. Most of the answers are word family or sight words from Unit 1.

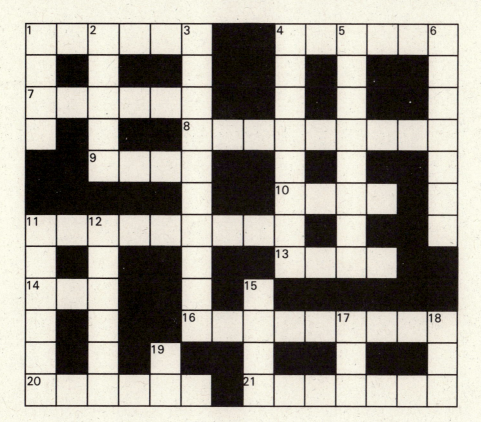

Across

1. The capital of Canada
4. What a butterfly comes out of
7. Most accurate or real
8. Entertainment
9. Belonging to you
10. Unable to speak
11. Thankfulness
13. Impolite
14. A homonym for ewe
16. A country that is a continent
20. To begin again
21. Used for washing hair

Down

1. Upon: He drove ___ the bridge.
2. Really
3. A continent largely covered with ice
4. A person who buys and uses things
5. Traveled back and forth to work
6. Not interfering or taking sides
11. Old Faithful is one of these
12. Mistreats
15. Operates; makes use of
17. The body part that the hand is attached to
18. Commotion
19. The contraction for I am

Lesson 6

The Word Families *ea, ei, eigh,* and *ey*

Sight Words			
ballet	crochet	café	fiancé
buffet	gourmet	sauté	fiancée

Word Families

ea
as /ā/

ei
as /ā/

eigh
as /ā/

ey
as /ā/

1 Listening

Listen to the sound of *ea* in these words.

great	break	daybreak	Great Plains
steak	breakdown	outbreak	Great Britain

Listen to the sound of *ei* in these words.

veil	rein	reign	feint
vein	reindeer	beige	

Listen to the sound of *eigh* in these words.

weigh	eight	sleigh	neighbor
weight	eighth	freight	neighborhood

Listen to the sound of *ey* in these words.

hey	prey	survey
they	obey	convey

2 Writing Words. On the lines below, write the words that you hear.

1. _____   5. _____   9. _____

2. _____   6. _____   10. _____

3. _____   7. _____   11. _____

4. _____   8. _____   12. _____

3 **Dictionary Skills: Word Origins.** Look up each of the sight words below. Underline the letters that spell long *a* at the end of each word. On the line beside the word, write the language from which the word comes. Then fill in the blanks in the pattern below.

1. ballet _____   5. café _____

2. buffet _____   6. fiancé _____

3. crochet _____   7. fiancée _____

4. gourmet _____   8. sauté _____

    Pattern: Long *a* can be spelled _____, _____, or _____ at the

        end of words taken from _____.

4 **Homonyms: *Fiancé* and *Fiancée*.** Write the meanings of these sight words on the lines provided.

fiancé _____

fiancée _____

What is the difference in the spelling of these two words?

_____

5 **Dictionary Skills: More Homonyms.** Answer the following questions using a dictionary if necessary.

1. Do you eat *stake* or *steak*? _____

2. Did the glass *brake* or *break*? _____

3. Does a bride wear a *vale* or a *veil*? _____

4. Is a blood vessel a *vain* or a *vein*? _____

5. Do you control a horse with *rains*, *reigns* or *reins*? _____

6. Is an action intended to mislead you a *faint* or a *feint*? _____

7. Is an eagle a bird of *pray* or of *prey*? _____

8. To make very small pieces, do you *grate* or *great* something? _____

6 **Word Building: Compound Words.** Form compound words by adding *break*, *great*, or *weight* to the beginning or end of each word below. Check your dictionary to see if your compounds are closed, hyphenated, or open.

1. up _____
2. under _____
3. Dane _____
4. heart _____
5. paper _____

6. neck _____
7. light _____
8. through _____
9. over _____
10. grandchild _____

7 **Spelling Long *a*.** All of the word families in this lesson spell long *a*. Four other ways to spell long *a* are listed below. Beside each spelling is an example. On the lines provided, write two more examples of words with each spelling.

Spelling	Example	Your Examples	
1. aCe	made	_____	_____
2. aiC	aim	_____	_____
3. ay	day	_____	_____
4. aCy	scary	_____	_____

8 **Reviewing a Pattern: Changing *y* to *i*.** When adding an ending to a word that ends in **C**y, change the *y* to *i* unless the ending begins with *i*. If there is a vowel before the *y*, do not change the *y* to *i*. Add the endings to the words below following this pattern.

1. duty + ful _____
2. cry + ing _____
3. obey + ed _____
4. survey + or _____
5. try + ed _____

6. weighty + er _____
7. prey + ing _____
8. droopy + est _____
9. convey + ance _____
10. apply + ing _____

9 **Writing Sentences.** On the lines below, write the sentences that you hear.

1. _____

2. _____

3. _____

4. _____

5. _____

_____

6. _____

_____

10 **Puzzle.** Use the clues below to fill in the blocks of this puzzle. All of the answer words are representative words from this lesson. When you have filled in all the correct answers, the letters in the shaded blocks will spell another *eigh* word.

Clues

1. To follow a command or request

2. To determine the boundaries of land

3. A sudden eruption, as of a disease

4. The heaviness of something

5. Straps used to control horses

6. What a bride wears over her face

7. A light brown color

8. The plural of *he*, *she*, or *it*

The new *eigh* word: _____

Lesson 7

The Word Families *ie*, *ei*, *i*, and *iCe*

Sight Words		
antique	technique	fatigue
unique		intrigue

Word Families

1 **Listening**

ie
as /ē/

Listen to the sound of *ie* in these words.

brief	field	thief	movie
grief	yield	relief	series
belief	niece	relieve	calorie
believe	piece	achievement	prairie

ei
as /ē/

Listen to the sound of *ei* in these words.

seize	either	receive	deceit
ceiling	neither	conceive	protein
leisure	receipt	perceive	caffeine

i
as /ē/

Listen to the sound of *i* in these words.

ski	trio	exterior
taxi	kilo	interior
chili	liter	superior

iCe
as /ēC/

Listen to the sound of *iCe* in these words.

marine	vaccine	elite	police
magazine	routine	petite	prestige
quarantine	gasoline	figurine	automobile

2 **Writing Words.** On the lines below, write the words that you hear.

1. _____ 4. _____ 7. _____

2. _____ 5. _____ 8. _____

3. _____ 6. _____ 9. _____

3 **Using Sight Words.** Like the sight words in Lessons 5 and 6, all the sight words in this lesson have come into English through French. Underline the last three letters in each word below and answer the questions that follow.

antique   technique   unique   fatigue   intrigue

1. What letters spell /k/ at the end of the first three words? _____

2. What letters spell /g/ at the end of the last two words? _____

3. What letter spells long *e* in each of these words? _____

Use two of the sight words in original sentences.

_____

_____

4 **Dictionary Skills: Alternative Spellings for Long *e*.** Each of the words spelled phonetically below contains one of the long *e* spellings in this lesson. Use the dictionary to find the correct spelling. When you find the spelling that matches the definition given, write the word on the line provided.

Phonetic Spelling	Definition	Correct Spelling
1. /shēld/	a means of protection or defense	_____
2. /lē′tər/	a measure of volume in the metric system	_____
3. /chēf/	highest in rank; most important	_____
4. /sŭb′mə rēn/	a ship that operates under water	_____
5. /dē sēv/	to mislead, delude, or lie	_____

5 **Word Building.** Fill in *ei*, *ie*, or *i* to correctly spell long *e* in each word below. Then write the entire word on the line provided.

1. retr_____ve _____

2. crit_____que _____

3. disbel_____f _____

4. s_____zure _____

5. infer_____or _____

6. conc_____t _____

7. shr_____k _____

8. rad_____us _____

9. outf_____lder _____

10. rec_____ver _____

6 **Alternative Spellings for Long *e*: *ei* and *ie*.** Long *e* can be spelled both *ei* and *ie*. If long *e* is spelled *ei* in the words or phrases your teacher dictates, write them in the **ei** column. Write them in the **ie** column if long *e* is spelled *ie*.

ei	ie
_____	_____
_____	_____
_____	_____
_____	_____

7 **Spelling Long *e*.** All of the word families in this lesson contain long *e* spellings. Six other ways to spell long *e* are listed below. Beside each spelling is an example. On the lines provided, write two more examples of words with each spelling.

Spelling	Example	Your Examples	
1. e	be	_____	_____
2. ee	feel	_____	_____
3. ea	eat	_____	_____
4. ey	money	_____	_____
5. y	any	_____	_____
6. eCe	here	_____	_____

8 **Homonyms: *Peace* and *Piece*.** Use *peace* and *piece* in original sentences.

peace _____

piece _____

9 **Finding Patterns.** In this lesson, you learned that *ie* spells long *e*. However, there are a few words in which *ie* spells long *i*. Follow the steps below to discover two patterns regarding these words.

Part A. Underline *ie* in the following words and complete the pattern.

die   hie   lie   pie   tie   vie

Pattern: In three-letter words that end in *ie*, *ie* spells long _____.

Part B. Build the words indicated below and complete the pattern. Use your dictionary if necessary.

1. die + ing   _____   3. tie + ing   _____

2. lie + ing   _____   4. vie + ing   _____

Pattern: When *-ing* is added to three-letter words that end in *ie*,

change the *ie* to _____ before adding *-ing*.

10 **Writing Sentences.** On the lines below, write the sentences that you hear.

1. _____

2. _____

3. _____

4. _____

5. _____

6. _____

7. _____

Lesson 8

The Word Families *ough*, *oul*, *ost*, and *olk*

Sight Words			
beau	plateau	sew	patrol
bureau	tableau	gross	control

Word Families

ough
as /ō/

oul
as /ōl/

ost
as /ōst/

olk
as /ōk/

❶ Listening

Listen to the sound of *ough* in these words.

though	dough	borough	thorough
although	doughnut	furlough	thoroughly
			thoroughfare

Listen to the sound of *oul* in these words.

soul	boulder	poultry
soulful	shoulder	

Listen to the sound of *ost* in these words.

most	post	poster	foremost
almost	host	postage	guidepost
mostly	ghost	postpone	innermost

Listen to the sound of *olk* in these words.

yolk	polka	folklore
folks	polka dot	folk song

❷ Writing Words. On the lines below, write the words that you hear.

1. _____   4. _____   7. _____

2. _____   5. _____   8. _____

3. _____   6. _____   9. _____

3 Dictionary Skills: Word Origins

Part A. Look up the sight words below and write the language from which each word came on the line beside it. Underline the letters that spell long *o* in each word.

1. beau _____   3. plateau _____

2. bureau _____   4. tableau _____

How is long *o* spelled at the end of these words? _____

Part B. Look up the words below and write the language from which each word came on the line beside it. Underline the letters that spell long *o* in each word.

1. mauve _____   3. chauffeur _____

2. taupe _____   4. chauvinist _____

How is long *o* spelled in these words? _____

    Pattern: Long *o* can be spelled _____ or _____ in words

        taken from _____.

4 Alternative Spellings for Long *o*.

All the word families in this lesson contain long *o* spellings. Write the phrases that your teacher dictates in the appropriate column below.

ough	**oul**
_____	_____
_____	_____
_____	_____
ost	**olk**
_____	_____
_____	_____

5 **Spelling Long *o*.** All of the word families in this lesson spell long *o*. Eight other ways to spell long *o* are listed below. Beside each spelling is an example. On the lines provided, write another example of a word with each spelling.

Spelling	Example	Your Example	Spelling	Example	Your Example
1. oCe	sole	_____	5. o	go	_____
2. oaC	boat	_____	6. oe	doe	_____
3. oll	roll	_____	7. ow	blow	_____
4. olC	cold	_____	8. own	flown	_____

6 **Proofreading.** It is sometimes hard to know which spelling to use when you hear the long *o* sound. Each of the words below is spelled two ways. Underline the one that you think is correct. Then look up the word in your dictionary to be sure you are right. When you have checked the spelling, write the word on the line provided.

1. thow	though	_____
2. postage	poastage	_____
3. although	althoe	_____
4. polka	poka	_____
5. thorow	thorough	_____
6. shoulder	sholder	_____

7 **Dictionary Skills: Homonyms.** Answer the questions below, using a dictionary when necessary.

1. Are cookies made of *doe* or *dough*? _____

2. Are towns in some states called *boroughs* or *burrows*? _____

3. Is the bottom of a shoe a *sole* or a *soul*? _____

4. Is a huge rock a *bolder* or a *boulder*? _____

5. Is a device that joins a pair of animals a *yoke* or a *yolk*? _____

8 **Writing Sentences.** On the lines below, write the sentences that you hear.

1. _____

2. _____

3. _____

4. _____

5. _____

6. _____

7. _____

_____

9 **Puzzle.** Use the clues below to fill in the blocks of the puzzle. All of the answer words are representative or sight words from this lesson. When you have filled in all the correct answers, the letters in the shaded blocks will spell the name of a melon that has an unusual spelling for long *o*.

Clues

1. Power to direct or manage

2. Very nearly

3. Fried cake with a hole in the middle

4. A man who has guests

5. A lively dance

6. A leave granted to a soldier

7. Complete in every respect

8. Nevertheless; however

9. To put off until later

10. First in importance

The name of the melon: _____

Review of Unit 2

Other Spellings for Long Vowel Sounds

1 **Spelling Long *a***

Part A. Under each of the spellings below, write three words that contain that spelling for long *a*.

ea	ei	eigh	ey
_____	_____	_____	_____
_____	_____	_____	_____
_____	_____	_____	_____

Part B. Write two words that contain each of the long *a* spellings listed below.

1. aCe   _____   _____

2. aiC   _____   _____

3. ay   _____   _____

4. aCy   _____   _____

2 **Review of French Spellings.** Below are some words taken from French that you have studied in this unit. Review them and fill in the blanks in the patterns below.

buffet	café	unique	bureau
crochet	sauté	antique	plateau
gourmet	fiancée	fatigue	chauffeur

1. In words taken from French, long *a* at the end of words can be spelled _____, _____, or _____.

2. In words taken from French, /ēk/ and /ēg/ at the end of words can be spelled _____ and _____.

3. In words taken from French, long *o* can be spelled _____ or _____.

3 Spelling Long *e*

Part A. Under each of the spellings below, write three words that contain that spelling for long *e*.

ie	ei	i	iCe
_____	_____	_____	_____
_____	_____	_____	_____
_____	_____	_____	_____

Part B. Write one word that contains each of the long *e* spellings listed below.

1. e   _____
2. ee   _____
3. ea   _____

4. ey   _____
5. y   _____
6. eCe   _____

4 Spelling Long *o*

Part A. Under each of the spellings below, write three words that contain that spelling for long *o*.

ough	oul	ost	olk
_____	_____	_____	_____
_____	_____	_____	_____
_____	_____	_____	_____

Part B. Write one word that contains each of the long *o* spellings listed below.

1. oCe   _____
2. oaC   _____
3. oll   _____
4. olC   _____

5. o   _____
6. oe   _____
7. ow   _____
8. own   _____

5 **Word Building.** Fill in the blanks in the words below with either *ei* or *ie* to spell words that contain long *e*.

1. There is a large crack in the livingroom c__ __ling.

2. We never seem to have enough l__ __sure time.

3. How many letters did you rec__ __ve while you were away?

4. I don't bel__ __ve I've met that man before.

5. My n__ __ce is coming for Thanksgiving.

6. That jigsaw puzzle has a p__ __ce missing.

7. Judy was rel__ __ved when her lost pocketbook was returned.

8. We don't have much business to cover, so the meeting will be br__ __f.

6 **Homonym Review.** Use each of the homonyms below in an original sentence.

1. break _____

2. veil _____

3. vein _____

4. prey _____

5. great _____

6. steak _____

7 **Writing Sentences.** On the lines below, write the sentences that you hear.

1. _____

2. _____

3. _____

4. _____

_____

8 **Crossword Puzzle.** Use the clues below to complete this crossword puzzle. Most of the answers are word family or sight words from Unit 2.

Across

1. Having a small figure
4. These hold up wooden fences.
6. To travel over snow on long, flat runners
7. The opposite of exterior
8. The abbreviation for Place
10. A small, carved statue
12. To follow orders
13. Gives up; gives the right of way
15. The number after seven
19. A signal to begin; a reminder or hint
20. A sudden bursting forth, as of a disease
23. Tiredness
24. A homonym for sole

Down

1. To put off until later
2. A group of three
3. A person who steals
4. Takes for granted; supposes
5. Things happening one after another: baseball's World ___
9. The abbreviation for pound
11. Covered with frozen water
14. A homonym of dew
16. A homonym of grate
17. Nevertheless; however
18. Coarse; disgusting or repulsive
19. A French word for restaurant
21. The plural of he, she, or it
22. A metric weight equal to about 2.2 pounds

Lesson 9

The Word Families *er*, *ir*, and *ur*

Word Families

er as /ûr/

ir as /ûr/

ur as /ûr/

❶ Listening

Listen to the sound of *er* in these words.

hers	exert	allergy	emergency
term	desert	fertile	determined
nervous	dessert	vertical	interpret
service	concert	permanent	remember

Listen to the sound of *ir* in these words.

sir	bird	firm	irk
stir	birth	affirm	quirk
circle	flirt	confirm	shirk
circus	squirt	infirmary	smirk

Listen to the sound of *ur* in these words.

fur	hurt	curve	urban
blur	injury	burnt	suburb
spur	furnish	urgent	current
occur	return	surgery	purchase

❷ Writing Words. On the lines below, write the words that you hear.

1. _____   4. _____   7. _____

2. _____   5. _____   8. _____

3. _____   6. _____   9. _____

3 **Emergency Numbers.** Make a list of the telephone numbers of services that you might have to contact in an emergency. List some of the health words in this lesson. Don't forget the police and fire departments.

Service	Phone Number	Service	Phone Number
_____	____-_____	_____	____-_____
_____	____-_____	_____	____-_____
_____	____-_____	_____	____-_____

4 **Proofreading.** It is sometimes hard to know which spelling to use when you hear the sound /ûr/. Each of the words below is spelled two ways. Underline the one that you think is correct. Then look up the word in your dictionary to be sure you are right. When you have checked the spelling, write the word on the line provided.

1. burthday   birthday   _____

2. purpose   perpose   _____

3. Saterday   Saturday   _____

4. nersery   nursery   _____

5. perfume   purfume   _____

5 **Reviewing Doubling Patterns 1 and 2.** Add the endings below, doubling the final consonants when necessary.

1. stir + ing   _____   6. spur + ed   _____

2. blur + y   _____   7. occur + ence   _____

3. irk + ed   _____   8. prefer + ing   _____

4. refer + al   _____   9. smirk + ed   _____

5. confirm + ed   _____   10. whir + ing   _____

Use one of the words you formed in an original sentence.

_____

6 **Reviewing Syllable Types.** The five types of syllables you have studied are listed below. An example of each type is given. Write two more examples of each type of syllable on the lines provided.

Syllable Type	Example	Your Examples	
1. Closed	mit	_____	_____
2. Open	se	_____	_____
3. Cle	ple	_____	_____
4. VCe	use	_____	_____
5. Double Vowel	oom	_____	_____

7 **Another Syllable Type.** Another type of syllable is called the r-controlled syllable. An r-controlled syllable has one or two vowels followed by an *r*. When an *r* follows a vowel, it changes the sound of the vowel somewhat. Write the dictated words containing r-controlled syllables under the correct headings.

er	ir	ur
_____	_____	_____
_____	_____	_____
_____	_____	_____

8 **Writing Words by Syllables.** Write the words your teacher dictates by syllables. Then write the entire word on the line provided.

	First Syllable	Second Syllable	Third Syllable	Fourth Syllable	Whole Word
1.	_____	_____	_____		_____
2.	_____	_____	_____		_____
3.	_____	_____	_____		_____
4.	_____	_____	_____		_____
5.	_____	_____	_____		_____

9 *Desert* **and** *Dessert*. When the accent falls on the second syllable, *desert* is a homonym of *dessert*. When the accent falls on the first syllable, *desert* and *dessert* sound almost alike, and people tend to confuse their spellings. Study the examples and then use each word in an original sentence.

Examples: 1. The *desert* is very dry.
            2. Don't *desert* us when we need you.
            3. They had apple pie and ice cream for *dessert*.

1. desert (dĕz´ərt) _____

2. desert (dĭ zûrt´) _____

3. dessert _____

10 **Review of a Pattern with Meaning: -er.** The suffix *-er* indicates a person or thing that does something. Add *-er* to these words.

1. troop	_____	6. roof	_____
2. vote	_____	7. remove	_____
3. mow	_____	8. intrude	_____
4. produce	_____	9. receive	_____
5. interpret	_____	10. desert	_____

11 **Writing Sentences.** On the lines below, write the sentences that you hear.

1. _____

2. _____

3. _____

4. _____

5. _____

6. _____

_____

Lesson 10

The Word Families *or*, *our*, *ear*, and *ar*

Health Words

hygiene	virus	poison
infection	bacteria	seizure

Word Families

or
as /ûr/
and /ər/

our
as /ûr/

ear
as /ûr/

ar
as /ər/

1 Listening

Listen to the sound of *or* in these words.

word	work	honor	doctor
world	worth	error	flavor
worst	worry	mirror	favorite

Listen to the sound of *our* in these words.

journey	courage	nourish
journal	discourage	flourish
adjourn	encouragement	courtesy

Listen to the sound of *ear* in these words.

earl	earth	search	heard
early	earnest	research	rehearse

Listen to the sound of *ar* in these words.

collar	hazard	awkward	popular
dollar	mustard	forward	regular
cellar	blizzard	backwards	circular

2 Writing Words. On the lines below, write the words that you hear.

1. _____
2. _____
3. _____

4. _____
5. _____
6. _____

7. _____
8. _____
9. _____

3 Using Health Words. Suppose you missed several days of work because you or someone in your family had an accident or illness. Write a report to your supervisor explaining this. Use some of the health words from Lessons 9 and 10 in your report.

_____

_____

_____

_____

_____

4 Word Building. Write the missing syllable of each word you hear.

1. en _____ age
2. fa _____ ite
3. _____ nest ly

4. cir cu _____
5. ad _____ ment
6. pop _____ lar

7. _____ hears al
8. hon _____ a ble
9. ra di a _____

5 Patterns with Meaning: -or. Like -er, the suffix -or is added to words to indicate a person or thing that does something. The suffix -or is added to many verbs that end in _ate_ to indicate the person or thing that does the action. Write the nouns formed by adding -or to the verbs below.

1. illustrate _____
2. decorate _____
3. elevate _____
4. translate _____
5. legislate _____

6. refrigerate _____
7. navigate _____
8. operate _____
9. investigate _____
10. escalate _____

Use three of the words you formed in original sentences.

_____

_____

_____

6 **R-Controlled Syllables as Endings.** Many words end with *er*, *or*, or *ar*. When these syllables are not accented, they usually sound alike.

Part A. Write either *er*, *or*, or *ar* in the blanks below. Check any spellings you are not sure of in your dictionary.

1. edit_____   6. mot_____   11. sail_____   16. pap_____

2. jok_____   7. popul_____   12. weld_____   17. simil_____

3. visit_____   8. hamm_____   13. lett_____   18. calend_____

4. doll_____   9. act_____   14. invent_____   19. conduct_____

5. dinn_____   10. off_____   15. fath_____   20. dang_____

Part B. Now write each of the words you formed in the appropriate column below.

er	or	ar
_____	_____	_____
_____	_____	_____
_____	_____	_____
_____	_____	
_____	_____	
_____	_____	
_____		
_____		

Part C. Based on the number of words under each heading above, fill in the blanks in these statements.

1. The most common way to spell /ər/ at the end of a word is _____.

2. The spelling that often follows the letter *t* is _____.

3. The least likely spelling of /ər/ at the end of a word is _____.

7 **Writing Sentences.** On the lines below, write the sentences that you hear.

1. _____
2. _____
3. _____
4. _____
5. _____
   _____
6. _____
   _____

8 **Puzzle.** Use the clues below to fill in the blocks of the puzzle. All of the answer words are representative words from this lesson. When you have filled in all the correct answers, the letters in the shaded blocks will spell a new word ending in / ər / .

Clues

1. Well-liked; having many friends

2. Clumsy; not graceful

3. Ahead of time

4. Consideration for others

5. Best liked; first choice

6. Shaped like a circle

7. A daily record of events

8. One hundred cents

9. Past tense of *hear*

10. A mistake

The new word: _____

Lesson 11

The Word Families *arr*, *ar*, and *ear*

Health Words		
hepatitis	tonsillitis	rubella
arthritis	appendicitis	pneumonia

Word Families

arr
as /ăr/

ar
as /âr/

ear
as /âr/

1 Listening

Listen to the sound of *arr* in these words.

carry	arrow	barrel	carrot
marry	narrow	barren	parrot
carriage	narrator	barrier	arrogant
marriage	narration	embarrass	

Listen to the sound of *ar* in these words.

wary	parent	hilarious	librarian
vary	transparent	vicarious	vegetarian
variation	scarcity	precarious	humanitarian

Listen to the sound of *ear* in these words.

bear	pear	wear	overbearing
bearer	tear	swear	underwear

2 Writing Words. On the lines below, write the words that you hear.

1. _____   5. _____   9. _____

2. _____   6. _____   10. _____

3. _____   7. _____   11. _____

4. _____   8. _____   12. _____

3 **Word Building.** Fill in *arr*, *ar*, or *ear* in each blank below to correctly spell words containing /ăr/ or /âr/. Then write the entire word on the line provided. Use your dictionary if necessary.

1. qu_____y _____
2. _____ea _____
3. n_____ate _____
4. can_____y _____
5. p_____ _____
6. c_____iage _____
7. forsw_____ _____

8. transp_____ent _____
9. hil_____ity _____
10. prec_____ious _____
11. underw_____ _____
12. planet_____ium _____
13. humanit_____ian _____
14. emb_____assment _____

4 **Writing Words by Syllables.** Write the words your teacher dictates by syllables. Then write the entire word on the line provided.

First Syllable	Second Syllable	Third Syllable	Fourth Syllable	Whole Word
1. _____	_____	_____		_____
2. _____	_____	_____		_____
3. _____	_____	_____		_____
4. _____	_____	_____		_____
5. _____	_____	_____		_____
6. _____	_____	_____	_____	_____
7. _____	_____	_____	_____	_____
8. _____	_____	_____	_____	_____

Use two of the words you wrote in original sentences.

_____

_____

5 **Dictionary Skills: Homonyms.** Answer the following questions, using a dictionary if necessary.

1. Is a large animal covered with fur a *bare* or a *bear*? _____

2. Do you have a *pair*, a *pare*, or a *pear* of shoes? _____

3. Are items for sale *wares* or *wears*? _____

4. Is a sweet, juicy fruit a *pare* or a *pear*? _____

5. When you carry something, do you *bare* it or *bear* it? _____

6. When you put on your coat, do you *ware* it or *wear* it? _____

6 **Word Building with *There* and *Where*.** The sound /âr/ is spelled *ere* in *there* and *where*. Many compound words are formed using these two words. Add either *there* or *where* to the beginning or end of the words below to form compound words.

1. ever _____   6. any _____

2. fore _____   7. after _____

3. some _____   8. in _____

4. every _____   9. else _____

5. upon _____   10. abouts _____

7 **Writing Sentences.** On the lines below, write the sentences that you hear.

1. _____

2. _____

3. _____

4. _____

5. _____

6. _____

_____

8 **Personal Health Words.** On the lines below, list any health-related words that apply to you. Use a dictionary to check your spellings.

1. Illnesses or conditions I currently have:

_____

2. Illnesses or conditions I have had in the past:

_____

3. Operations or injuries I have had in the past:

_____

9 **Filling out Forms.** Below is a section of a medical history form. Fill it out using some of the sight words from this lesson or your personal health words.

Goodfellow Health Clinic
Personal Medical History

Patient Name: _____ Date: ___/___/___

Address: _____ Phone: ____-_____

City and State: _____ Date of Birth: ___/___/___

1. What childhood diseases did you have?

_____

2. What illnesses or conditions have you received medical treatment for in the last five years? (give dates)

_____

_____

3. What illnesses have your parents and siblings had?

_____

_____

Lesson 12

The Word Families *er*, *err*, *er*, and *ere*

Sight Words

heir	pier	lyric	tyranny
weird	tier	irritate	pyramid

Word Families

er
as /ĕr/

err
as /ĕr/

er
as /îr/

ere
as /îr/

1 Listening

Listen to the sound of *er* in these words.

very	American	sheriff	cherish
verify	heritage	stereo	perishable
merit	ceremony	sterilize	clerical
peril	serenade	therapy	geriatric

Listen to the sound of *err* in these words.

errand	terrace	herring	cherry
error	terrified	derrick	raspberry
terror	territory	serrated	ferris wheel

Listen to the sound of *er* in these words.

hero	series	inferior	material
zero	serial	superior	bacteria
cereal	serious	exterior	cafeteria
period	mysterious	experience	deteriorate

Listen to the sound of *ere* in these words.

here	severe	sphere
adhere	sincere	hemisphere
merely	interfere	atmosphere

2 **Writing Words.** On the lines below, write the words that you hear.

1. _____   5. _____   9. _____

2. _____   6. _____   10. _____

3. _____   7. _____   11. _____

4. _____   8. _____   12. _____

3 **Alternative Spellings for /ĕr/.** The sound /ĕr/ is commonly spelled *er* and *err*. If the words or phrases your teacher dictates contain *er*, write them in the **er** column. Write them in the **err** column if they contain *err*.

er	err
_____	_____
_____	_____
_____	_____
_____	_____

4 **Dictionary Skills: Finding the Correct Spelling.** There are two common spellings for /îr/: *er* and *ere*. In a few words, /îr/ is spelled *ir*. A dictionary can help you find the correct spelling. The words spelled phonetically below contain the sound /îr/. Use the dictionary to find the correct spellings and write them on the lines provided.

Phonetic Spelling	Definition	Correct Spelling
1. /ăd hîr´ ənt/	a loyal follower	_____
2. /pîr ē ŏd´ ĭk/	happening at regular intervals	_____
3. /rĕ vîr´/	to regard with great respect or reverence	_____
4. /îr´ ĭ gāt/	to supply water to land or crops	_____
5. /ĭn tîr´ ē ər/	the inner part; inside	_____

5 **Alternative Sounds for _er_.** You have learned that _er_ spells three different sounds: /ûr/ as in _her_, /ĕr/ as in _very_, and /îr/ as in _hero_. Write each word below under the appropriate heading.

concerted   kerosene   personnel   sterile
detergent   periodical   seriousness   sterling
interior   periscope   stereotype   superiority

/ûr/ as in _her_   **/ĕr/ as in _very_**   **/îr/ as in _hero_**

_____   _____   _____

_____   _____   _____

_____   _____   _____

_____   _____   _____

6 **Homonyms and Almost Homonyms.** Some of the sight words and family words in this lesson have homonyms. For others, there are words that sound almost the same. Use each of the words below in an original sentence.

1. heir _____

   air _____

2. very _____

   vary _____

3. berry _____

   bury _____

4. here _____

   hear _____

5. pier _____

   peer _____

6. cereal _____

   serial _____

7 Review of the Possessive Apostrophe. An apostrophe (') is used to show ownership or possession. Follow the steps below to spell the possessive forms of nouns.

Step 1. Write the owner(s) or possessors(s).

the boss   the people   the parents

Step 2. Add an apostrophe.

the boss'   the people'   the parents'

Step 3. Add an *s* if you can hear an *s* when you say the phrase.

the boss's orders   the people's choice   the parents' permission

Rewrite the phrases below using an apostrophe to show possession.

1. the eggs of the goose   _____

2. the routine of the men   _____

3. the uniforms of the officers   _____

4. the badges of the sheriffs   _____

5. the argument of the prosecutor _____

6. the anniversary of the Perrys   _____

8 Writing Sentences. On the lines below, write the sentences that you hear.

1. _____

2. _____

3. _____

4. _____

5. _____

_____

6. _____

_____

Lesson 13

The Word Families *or*, *oar*, *our*, and *ar*

Sight Words			
aura	dinosaur	boor	moor

Word Families

or as /ôr/

1 Listening

Listen to the sound of *or* in these words.

order	born	glory	florist
organ	horn	story	historian
organize	corner	inventory	pictorial
ordinary	former	mandatory	victorious

oar as /ôr/

Listen to the sound of *oar* in these words.

oar	boar	hoard	roar
soar	aboard	hoarse	uproar

our as /ôr/

Listen to the sound of *our* in these words.

pour	gourd	courtship	recourse
fourth	mourn	courthouse	resourceful

ar as /ôr/

Listen to the sound of *ar* in these words.

war	warm	thwart	quart
ward	swarm	warrant	quarter
reward	swarthy	warning	quarrel

2 Writing Words. On the lines below, write the words that you hear.

1. _____   4. _____   7. _____

2. _____   5. _____   8. _____

3. _____   6. _____   9. _____

6 **Proofreading.** In this lesson there are four ways to spell /ôr/. Another spelling for /ôr/, *ore*, was introduced in Book 2. It is sometimes hard to know which spelling to use when you hear the sound /ôr/. Each of the words below is written two ways. Underline the one that you think is correct. Then look up the word in your dictionary to be sure you are right. When you have checked the spelling, write the word on the line provided.

1. forgive   foregive   _____

2. soarce   source   _____

3. hoard   hord   _____

4. story   stoary   _____

5. coart   court   _____

6. roar   rore   _____

7. befor   before   _____

8. sworm   swarm   _____

7 **Word Building.** Write one of the word families below in each blank to complete a word that fits the context of the sentence.

or   ore   oar   our   ar

1. Ruby's baby was b_____n last night.

2. She teaches in the res_____ce room.

3. Have you placed your _____der yet?

4. Have you ever seen a hawk s_____ above a field?

5. Rudy applied f_____ a job at the c_____thouse.

6. Barry got a rew_____d when he returned the wallet he found.

7. Are you going to the st_____, _____ am I?

8. Doris and three other musicians have f_____med a qu_____tet.

8 **Writing Sentences.** On the lines below, write the sentences that you hear.

1. _____

2. _____

3. _____

4. _____

5. _____

6. _____

_____

9 **Composing Sentences.** On a separate sheet of paper, write two or three sentences about each of the pictures below. Use some of the listed words in your sentences.

American	carry	courage	Fourth of July	hero
award	ceremony	ferris wheel	glory	honor
birthday	cherish	flourish	heritage	service

Lesson 14

The Word Families *ar*, *ure*, and *our*

Sight Words		
hearth	sorry	amateur
hearty	sorrow	grandeur

Word Families

ar as /är/

ure as /yŏŏr/ or /ŏŏr/

our as /ŏŏr/

① Listening

Listen to the sound of *ar* in these words.

far	art	arm	bark
jar	party	charm	mark
mar	depart	card	arctic
star	partner	hardly	architect

Listen to the sound of *ure* in these words.

pure	endure	sure	lure
cure	mature	assure	figure
secure	obscure	insure	procedure

Listen to the sound of *our* in these words.

| your | tour | detour | courier |
| yourself | tourist | contour | gourmet |

② Writing Words. On the lines below, write the words that you hear.

1. _____   5. _____   9. _____

2. _____   6. _____   10. _____

3. _____   7. _____   11. _____

4. _____   8. _____   12. _____

3 **Alternative Spellings for /ŏŏr/.** The sound /ŏŏr/ is commonly spelled *ure* and *our*. If the words or phrases your teacher dictates contain *ure*, write them in the **ure** column. Write them in the **our** column if they contain *our*.

ure   our

_____   _____

_____   _____

_____   _____

_____   _____

4 **Alternative Sounds for *ar*.** You have learned that *ar* spells four different sounds: /ər/ as in *dollar*, /âr/ as in *parent*, /ôr/ as in *war*, and /är/ as in *far*. Write each word below under the appropriate heading.

archer	carpenter	invariable	quarter
bargain	daring	pillar	various
blizzard	disarmament	scholar	warmth
canary	forewarn	similar	wharf

/ər/ as in *dollar*   **/âr/ as in *parent***

_____   _____

_____   _____

_____   _____

_____   _____

/ôr/ as in *war*   **/är/ as in *far***

_____   _____

_____   _____

_____   _____

_____   _____

5 **Review of Syllable Types.** The six types of syllables that you have studied are listed below. An example of each type is given. Write another example of each type of syllable on the lines provided.

Syllable Type	Example	Your Example
1. Closed	ed	_____
2. Open	pro	_____
3. Cle	tle	_____
4. VCe	uce	_____
5. Double Vowel	eat	_____
6. R-Controlled	warm	_____

6 **Writing Words by Syllables.** Write the words your teacher dictates by syllables. Then write the entire word on the line provided.

	First Syllable	Second Syllable	Third Syllable	Fourth Syllable	Whole Word
1.	_____	_____			_____
2.	_____	_____	_____		_____
3.	_____	_____	_____		_____
4.	_____	_____	_____		_____
5.	_____	_____	_____		_____
6.	_____	_____	_____	_____	_____
7.	_____	_____	_____		_____
8.	_____	_____	_____	_____	_____
9.	_____	_____	_____	_____	_____

Use two of the words you wrote in original sentences.

_____

_____

7 **Writing Sentences.** On the lines below, write the sentences that you hear.

1. _____

2. _____

3. _____

4. _____

5. _____

6. _____

7. _____

_____

8 **Puzzle.** Use the clues below to fill in the blocks of the puzzle. All of the answer words are representative or sight words from this lesson. When you have filled in all the correct answers, the letters in the shaded blocks will spell a new *our* family word.

Clues

1. A person who designs buildings

2. A temporary route

3. To bear, tolerate, or put up with a hardship

4. A person who travels for pleasure

5. The outline or shape of a body or a figure

6. The floor of a fireplace

7. A person who appreciates fine food

8. To leave

9. Magnificence; splendor

10. A gathering of people for enjoyment

The new *our* word: _____

Review of Unit 3

R-Controlled Vowels

1 **Word Building.** Write the missing syllable in each word you hear.

1. de _____ mine
2. _____ ni ture
3. fa vor _____
4. af _____ ma tive

5. en _____ age
6. _____ ma nent
7. bliz _____
8. hi _____ i ous

9. _____ ger y
10. em _____ rass ment
11. _____ ish a ble
12. at mos _____

2 **Words That End in /ər/.** Fill in either *er*, *or*, or *ar* for each of the words below. When you are finished, check your answers in your dictionary.

1. fing_____
2. mirr_____
3. help_____
4. answ_____
5. corn_____
6. doll_____
7. dinn_____

8. hamm_____
9. err_____
10. partn_____
11. mot_____
12. wait_____
13. writ_____
14. roof_____

15. doct_____
16. plumb_____
17. Novemb_____
18. calend_____
19. murd_____
20. refrigerat_____
21. centimet_____

3 **Review of the Possessive Apostrophe.** Rewrite the phrases below using an apostrophe to show possession.

1. the plans of the tourists _____

2. the orders of the doctor _____

3. the injuries of the patients _____

4. the rotation of the earth _____

5. the worth of a dollar _____

4 **More Word Building.** Use the syllables in each group to build words. The number of blanks indicates the number of syllables in each word. The first one has been started for you.

part   de   al   ment   **Whole Word**

1. _de_ _part_ _____   _depart_

2. _de_ _part_ _ment_   _department_

3. _____ _____ _____   _____

re   ful   source   ness

1. _____ _____   _____

2. _____ _____   _____

3. _____ _____ _____ _____   _____

get   for   ness   ful

1. _____ _____   _____

2. _____ _____   _____

3. _____ _____ _____ _____   _____

per   al   i   ty   son

1. _____ _____   _____

2. _____ _____ _____   _____

3. _____ _____ _____ _____ _____   _____

5 **Review of Doubling Patterns.** Add the endings to the words below. Double the final consonant when necessary.

1. star + ing _____   5. refer + ing _____

2. fur + y _____   6. mar + ed _____

3. honor + ing _____   7. humor + ous _____

4. bear + able _____   8. prefer + ed _____

6 **Proofreading.** Each of the words below is written two ways. Underline the one that you think is correct. Then look up the word in your dictionary to be sure you are right. When you have checked the spelling, write the word on the line provided.

1. docter   doctor   _____

2. journey   jurney   _____

3. personal   pursonal   _____

4. erly   early   _____

5. wirth   worth   _____

6. doller   dollar   _____

7. calendar   calender   _____

8. similar   similer   _____

9. mustard   musterd   _____

10. very   verry   _____

7 **Homonym Review.** Write a sentence using each of the homonyms below.

1. bored   _____

2. board   _____

3. four   _____

4. for   _____

5. bare   _____

6. bear   _____

7. pear   _____

8. pare   _____

9. morning _____

10. mourning _____

8 **Writing Words by Syllables.** Write the words your teacher dictates by syllables. Then write the entire word on the line provided.

First Syllable	Second Syllable	Third Syllable	Fourth Syllable	Whole Word
1. _____	_____	_____		_____
2. _____	_____	_____		_____
3. _____	_____	_____		_____
4. _____	_____	_____	_____	_____
5. _____	_____	_____	_____	_____
6. _____	_____	_____	_____	_____
7. _____	_____	_____	_____	_____
8. _____	_____	_____	_____	_____

Use two of the words you wrote in original sentences.

_____

_____

9 **Writing Sentences.** On the lines below, write the sentences that you hear.

1. _____

2. _____

3. _____

4. _____

5. _____

_____

6. _____

_____

10 **Filling out Forms.** Below is the patient's section of a health insurance claim form. Fill out the form, using your own name and address. Make up the details of an imaginary illness or injury, or use a real one.

GROUP HEALTH INSURANCE CLAIM	
PATIENT INFORMATION	
Patient's Name (First, middle initial, last)	Patient's Date of Birth / /
Patient's Address (Street, city, state, ZIP code)	Patient's Sex __ Female __ Male
Patient's Relationship to Insured: __ Self __ Spouse __ Child __ Other	

Other Health Insurance Coverage (plan holder, plan name, address, and plan number)	Was Condition Related to:
	A. Patient's Employment
	    __ Yes __ No
	B. An Auto Accident
	    __ Yes __ No

DESCRIPTION OF ILLNESS OR INJURY	
Describe symptoms or injury. (Give dates. If injury, state how and where it occurred.)	
INSURED INFORMATION	
Insured's Name (First, middle initial, last)	I.D. # or Medicare #
Insured's Address (Street, city, state, ZIP code)	Plan #
I authorize payment of medical benefits to undersigned physician or supplier for service described on the next page. Signature (insured or authorized person) _____ Date _____	

11 **Crossword Puzzle.** Use the clues below to complete this crossword puzzle. Many of the answers are family words or sight words from Unit 3.

Across

1. A person who treats you when you are ill
4. A talking bird
7. Past tense of eat
9. The opposite of inferior
10. Only; simply; barely
11. Extreme fright
12. The opposite of wide
14. ___, two, three
17. Something to cook in: frying ___
18. What you hear with
19. The opposite of she
20. Someone who visits
25. A body part; a large musical instrument
26. The ninth month

Down

1. Hot, dry places
2. To take a person prisoner
3. Tiny bits of rain
4. The opposite of temporary
5. To practice: ___ a play
6. The plural of he, she, or it
8. A homonym of too
13. Advance notice of danger
15. A thin piece of metal hammered into wood
16. The contraction for I have
19. Belonging to her
21. A smell
22. How old you are: What is your ___?
23. The opposite of down
24. The contraction for I am

Lesson 15

The Word Families *a*, *oll*, *olve*, and *ea*

Sight Words

garage	sabotage	suave
corsage	camouflage	

Word Families

a
as /ŏ/

oll
as /ŏl/

olve
as /ŏlv/

ea
as /ĕ/

1 Listening

Listen to the sound of *a* in these words.

wan	swap	quantity	wasp
want	swamp	quality	watch
wallet	swallow	equality	wad
wander	squabble	qualify	waddle

Listen to the sound of *oll* in these words.

doll	follow	jolly	holler
dollar	hollow	volley	pollen
collie	Holland	trolley	college

Listen to the sound of *olve* in these words.

solve	dissolve	involve
resolve		revolve

Listen to the sound of *ea* in these words.

head	bread	death	health
dead	spread	breath	sweater
dread	thread	feather	measure
ready	instead	weather	pleasure

2 **Writing Words.** On the lines below, write the words that you hear.

1. _____ 5. _____ 9. _____

2. _____ 6. _____ 10. _____

3. _____ 7. _____ 11. _____

4. _____ 8. _____ 12. _____

3 **Using Sight Words.** Fill in the blanks in the sentences below with the sight words from this lesson. Use each word only once.

1. Theresa's children got her a _____ for Mother's Day.

2. A chameleon can change color to _____ itself.

3. Does the Bernsteins' house have a two-car _____?

4. I hope you won't try to _____ our plans.

5. Polly's new friend is very _____.

4 **Word Building.** Fill in *a*, *oll*, or *olve* to correctly spell words with the short *o* sound.

1. c_____ar   5. w_____llow   9. w_____llet

2. qu_____lity   6. f_____y   10. rev_____d

3. h_____y   7. uns_____d   11. tr_____ey

4. diss_____   8. w_____nted   12. squ_____nder

5 **More Word Building.** Add the prefixes and suffixes to the words below following the patterns you have studied.

1. swap + ed   _____ 5. health + y + er   _____

2. involve + ment   _____ 6. ready + ness   _____

3. measure + able   _____ 7. in + equal + ity   _____

4. follow + ing   _____ 8. un + resolve + ed _____

6 **Homonyms.** Select the correct homonym in each of the sentences below and write it on the line provided.

1. That pipe is made of (led/lead).   _____

2. My favorite color is (red/read).   _____

3. We baked (bred/bread) yesterday.   _____

4. Have you (red/read) that book yet?   _____

5. The drum major (led/lead) the parade.   _____

6. Warren has (bred/bread) horses for many years.   _____

7 **Alternative Sounds for *ea* and *oll***

Part A. You have learned that *ea* spells three different sounds: /ē/ as in *sea*, /ā/ as in *great*, and /ĕ/ as in *head*. Write each word below under the appropriate heading.

appeal	outbreak	steak
heavy	reason	treasure
meant	repeat	yea

/ē/ as in *sea*	**/ā/ as in *great***	**/ĕ/ as in *head***
_____	_____	_____
_____	_____	_____
_____	_____	_____

Part B. You have learned that *oll* spells two sounds: /ōl/ as in *roll* and /ŏl/ as in *doll*. Write each listed word under the appropriate heading.

	/ōl/ as in *roll*	**/ŏl/ as in *doll***
enroll	_____	_____
holly		
knoll	_____	_____
lolling		
rollicking	_____	_____
stroll		

8 **Writing Sentences.** On the lines below, write the sentences that you hear.

1. _____
2. _____
3. _____
4. _____
5. _____
   _____
6. _____
   _____

9 **Puzzle.** Use the clues below to fill in the blocks of the puzzle. All of the answer words are compound words built with *head*. Refer to the list of answer words at the bottom of the page if necessary. When you have filled in all the correct answers, the letters in the shaded blocks will spell another *head* compound.

Clues

1. The operating expenses of a business

2. A marker for a grave

3. A pain in the head

4. Progress or forward motion

5. The title of a news story

6. With the head foremost

7. A leader who doesn't have real authority

8. A support for the head

9. A name and address printed on stationery

The new compound word with *head*: _____

Lesson 16

The Word Families *age*, *ate*, *ive*, and *iCe*

```
                    Sight Words
        minute     sieve        mischief
        business   privilege    handkerchief
```

Word Families

1 Listening

Listen to the sound of *age* in these words.

age
as /ĭj/

image	baggage	average	mileage
damage	cabbage	beverage	mortgage
manage	message	encourage	heritage
package	village	discourage	advantage

Listen to the sound of *ate* in these words.

ate
as /ĭt/

climate	accurate	separate	deliberate
private	adequate	ultimate	considerate
delicate	moderate	fortunate	appropriate

Listen to the sound of *ive* in these words.

ive
as /ĭv/

give	native	captive	fugitive
live	motive	festive	adjective
olive	positive	pensive	talkative
active	negative	incentive	tentative

Listen to the sound of *iCe* in these words.

iCe
as /ĭC/

office	famine	respite
notice	examine	infinite
justice	genuine	definite
practice	determine	exquisite

2 **Writing Words.** On the lines below, write the words that you hear.

1. _____   5. _____   9. _____

2. _____   6. _____   10. _____

3. _____   7. _____   11. _____

4. _____   8. _____   12. _____

3 **Word Building.** Fill in the missing syllables of the words that you hear.

1. prom _____   5. ju _____ nile   9. per cent _____

2. _____ ile   6. prej _____ dice   10. pos _____ sive

3. op po _____   7. fa vor _____   11. des per _____

4. mes _____   8. med i _____   12. cer tif i _____

Use two of the words you formed in original sentences.

_____

_____

4 **Alternative Spellings for /ĭt/.** The sound /ĭt/ at the end of words can be spelled *it*, *ate*, or *ite*. Write the words or phrases your teacher dictates in the appropriate column below.

      it   **ate**

_____   _____

_____   _____

_____   _____

      ite

_____

_____

_____

5 **Review of Syllable Types.** The six types of syllables you have studied are listed below. An example of each type is given. Write two more examples of each type of syllable on the lines provided.

Syllable Type	Example	Your Examples	
1. Closed	get	_____	_____
2. Open	se	_____	_____
3. Cle	cle	_____	_____
4. VCe	ade	_____	_____
5. Double Vowel	eam	_____	_____
6. R-Controlled	art	_____	_____

6 **Writing Words by Syllables.** Write the words your teacher dictates by syllables. Then write the entire word on the line provided.

	First Syllable	Second Syllable	Third Syllable	Fourth Syllable	Whole Word
1.	_____	_____			_____
2.	_____	_____			_____
3.	_____	_____			_____
4.	_____	_____			_____
5.	_____	_____	_____		_____
6.	_____	_____	_____		_____
7.	_____	_____	_____		_____
8.	_____	_____	_____	_____	_____
9.	_____	_____	_____	_____	_____
10.	_____	_____	_____	_____	_____

Use one of these words in an original sentence.

_____

7 **Review of Silent _e_ Patterns 1 and 2**

Part A. Silent _e_ Pattern 1: Drop a final silent _e_ when adding an ending that starts with a vowel.

Add the endings to the words below following Silent _e_ Pattern 1.

1. give + ing   _____   5. examine + ed   _____

2. live + able   _____   6. active + ity   _____

3. damage + ing   _____   7. manage + ment   _____

4. motive + ate   _____   8. practice + ing   _____

Part B. Answer the following questions to discover an exception to this pattern.

1. Write the root word for _mileage_. _____

2. Does the ending _-age_ begin with a consonant or a vowel? _____

3. What happens to the silent _e_ in _mile_ when _age_ is added? _____

Part C. Silent _e_ Pattern 2: When an ending that begins with _a_ or _o_ is added to a word that ends in _ce_ or _ge_, the silent _e_ is kept to retain the soft _c_ and _g_ sounds.

Add the endings to the words below following Silent _e_ Pattern 2.

1. courage + ous   _____   3. notice + able   _____

2. manage + able   _____   4. service + able   _____

8 **Writing Sentences.** On the lines below, write the sentences that you hear.

1. _____

2. _____

3. _____

4. _____

5. _____

     _____

Lesson 17

The Word Families *y*, *ain*, and *ui*

```
┌─────────────────────────────────┐
│            Food Words           │
│   recipe        squash          │
│   groceries     spinach         │
│   vegetables    broccoli        │
└─────────────────────────────────┘
```

Word Families

y
as /ĭ/

ain
as /ĭn/

ui
as /ĭ/

❶ Listening

Listen to the sound of *y* in these words.

gym	system	synonym	bicycle
hymn	symbol	syllable	physical
myth	symptom	sympathy	typical
rhythm	symphony	synagogue	mysterious

Listen to the sound of *ain* in these words.

bargain	fountain	certain	chaplain
captain	mountain	curtain	chieftain

Listen to the sound of *ui* in these words.

build	built	biscuit	guitar
building	guilt	circuit	guilty

❷ Writing Words. On the lines below, write the words that you hear.

1. _____   5. _____   9. _____

2. _____   6. _____   10. _____

3. _____   7. _____   11. _____

4. _____   8. _____   12. _____

3 **Making a Grocery List.** Imagine that you are going grocery shopping. Make out a list of items in the categories below. Write down items that you really use. Check your dictionary for any items you don't know how to spell.

Meat, Poultry, and Fish

1. _____

2. _____

3. _____

Dairy Products

1. _____

2. _____

3. _____

Frozen Foods

1. _____

2. _____

3. _____

Fresh Fruits and Vegetables

1. _____

2. _____

3. _____

Cereal and Baked Goods

1. _____

2. _____

3. _____

Canned Goods

1. _____

2. _____

3. _____

4 **Word Building.** Fill in the blanks in the words below with *y*, *ain*, or *ui* to correctly spell words with the short *i* sound.

1. Jessie is in the kitchen baking bisc_____ts for supper.

2. I cert_____ly would like to finish this project by tomorrow.

3. Ask Jim if he'll play his g_____tar at the party.

4. Julio has two extra tickets for the s_____mphony next week.

5. Maria is going to make new curt_____s for her room.

6. Do you know who wrote the l_____rics for that song?

7. The Turners will show slides from their trip to Eg_____pt.

8. They took many pictures of the p_____ramids.

5 **Proofreading.** Each of the words below is spelled two ways. Underline the one that you think is correct. Then look up the word in your dictionary to be sure you are right. When you have checked the spelling, write the word on the line provided.

1. bild   build   _____

2. mith   myth   _____

3. bargin   bargain   _____

4. tipical   typical   _____

5. biscuit   biskit   _____

6. mystery   mistery   _____

7. sertin   certain   _____

8. bicycle   bycicle   _____

6 **Alternative Sounds for y.** You have learned that *y* spells three different sounds: /ē/ as in *any*, /ī/ as in *cry*, and /ĭ/ as in *gym*. Write each word below under the appropriate heading.

already	identify	pretty	supply	try
February	July	reply	system	typical
homonym	library	rhythm	tricycle	worry

/ē/ as in *any*	/ī/ as in *cry*	/ĭ/ as in *gym*
_____	_____	_____
_____	_____	_____
_____	_____	_____
_____	_____	_____

7 **Review of Changing *ie* to *y*.** Change *ie* to *y* and add *-ing* to the words below.

1. die _____   2. tie _____   3. lie _____

8 **Writing Sentences.** On the lines below, write the sentences that you hear.

1. _____

2. _____

3. _____

4. _____
   _____

5. _____
   _____

9 **Composing a Paragraph.** On a separate sheet of paper, write a paragraph of five or six sentences about the scene below. Use some of the words from your grocery list in Exercise 3.

Lesson 18

The Word Families *o* and *ou*

Food Words

syrup	sausage	yogurt
pizza	bologna	margarine

Word Families

o
as /ŭ/

ou
as /ŭ/

1 Listening

Listen to the sound of *o* in these words.

son	money	other	oven
ton	front	brother	govern
month	among	another	above
wonder	become	nothing	shovel
tongue	stomach	dozen	discovery

Listen to the sound of *ou* in these words.

rough	couple	touch	young
tough	cousin	double	youngster
enough	country	trouble	southern

2 Writing Words. On the lines below, write the words that you hear.

1. _____   5. _____   9. _____

2. _____   6. _____   10. _____

3. _____   7. _____   11. _____

4. _____   8. _____   12. _____

3 Using Food Words. On the lines below, write menus for two dinners for you or your family. Specify what you would serve in each of the categories listed.

	Meal 1	Meal 2
Main Dish:	_____	_____
Salad/fruit/vegetable:	_____	_____
Bread/potatoes/rice:	_____	_____
Beverage and Dessert:	_____	_____

4 Word Building. Fill in the blanks in the words below with *o* or *ou* to correctly spell words with the short *u* sound.

1. Anton will be c_____ming to visit the Watsons next m_____nth.

2. Ramon has a c_____ple of c_____sins who can do that job for you.

3. I w_____nder what became of my _____ther gl_____ve.

4. Don't t_____ch the pan that just came out of the _____ven.

5. Will a d_____zen doughnuts be en_____gh?

6. Jason bit his t_____ngue when he stumbled on the fr_____nt steps.

7. Simon had a lot of tr_____ble with that t_____gh problem.

8. Marian was am_____ng five y_____g people who w_____n a trip to Washingt_____n, D.C.

5 Compound Words. Form compound words by adding *honey*, *money*, or *mother* to the beginning or end of each of the words below. Check your dictionary to see if your compounds are closed, hyphenated, or open.

1. changer _____
2. country _____
3. bee _____
4. tongue _____
5. comb _____
6. maker _____

6 **More Word Building.** Match a syllable from Column 2 with a syllable in Column 1 to make a word. Write the words on the lines provided. Check the spellings in your dictionary if necessary. Use each syllable in Column 1 only once.

Column 1   **Column 2**

bot	bon	1. _____
cus	dom	2. _____
lem	tom	3. _____
per	tom	4. _____
pri	tom	5. _____
rib	son	6. _____
sel	son	7. _____
symp	on	8. _____

7 **Alternative Spellings for the Schwa.** Each of the words you formed in Exercise 6 ends in an unaccented syllable. When the final syllable of a word is unaccented, the vowel is usually pronounced as a schwa. It is sometimes difficult to remember how the schwa is spelled. Write the words that you hear under the appropriate headings below.

an	**en**	**on**
_____	_____	_____
_____	_____	_____
_____	_____	_____
_____	_____	_____
_____	_____	_____
	_____	_____
	_____	

8 **Writing a Recipe.** On the card below, write one of your favorite recipes. List the necessary ingredients and their amounts, and give directions on how to make it.

Recipe Name: _____

Serves How Many: _____   Cooking Time: _____

_____

_____

_____

_____

_____

_____

_____

_____

_____

_____

_____

9 **Writing Sentences.** On the lines below, write the sentences that you hear.

1. _____

2. _____

3. _____

_____

4. _____

_____

5. _____

_____

Review of Unit 4

Other Spellings for Short Vowel Sounds

1 **Word Building.** Fill in the missing syllables of the words that you hear.

1. pos i _____   5. _____ la ble   9. bar _____

2. in _____ ment   6. cir _____   10. _____ ble some

3. av er _____   7. gen u _____   11. _____ ur y

4. e _____ i ty   8. dis _____ er   12. de lib er _____

2 **More Word Building.** Add the suffixes and prefixes to the words below.

1. wad + ed   _____   9. notice + able   _____

2. southern + er   _____   10. un + tie + ing   _____

3. lie + ing   _____   11. manage + ment   _____

4. wonder + ful   _____   12. in + justice   _____

5. double + ing   _____   13. damage + ing   _____

6. shovel + ed   _____   14. en + courage + ing _____

7. govern + ment   _____   15. un + qualify + ed _____

8. definite + ly   _____   16. imagine + a + tive _____

3 **Compound Words with *Head*.** Add *head* to the beginning or the end of the words below to form compound words. Check your dictionary to see if the compounds are closed, open, or hyphenated.

1. phone   _____   5. start   _____

2. strong   _____   6. fountain   _____

3. wind   _____   7. quarters   _____

4. bulk   _____   8. board   _____

④ Proofreading. Each of the words below is spelled two ways. Underline the one that you think is correct. Look up the word in your dictionary to be sure you are right. When you have checked the spelling, write the word on the line provided.

1. bargin   bargain   _____

2. weather   wether   _____

3. munny   money   _____

4. duble   double   _____

5. Monday   Munday   _____

6. swallow   swollow   _____

7. adequite   adequate   _____

8. ready   reddy   _____

9. cozin   cousin   _____

10. breth   breath   _____

⑤ Building Short *i* Words. Fill in the blanks in the words below with *a, i, ain, ui,* or *y* to correctly spell words containing the short *i* sound. Then write the words on the lines provided.

1. im_____ge   _____   9. s_____rup   _____

2. rh_____thm   _____   10. capt_____   _____

3. genu_____ne   _____   11. clim_____te _____

4. cert_____   _____   12. circ_____t   _____

5. priv_____te   _____   13. fount_____   _____

6. b_____ld   _____   14. bic_____cle _____

7. infin_____te _____   15. resp_____te _____

8. bisc_____t   _____   16. g_____lty   _____

6 **Finding Root Words.** On the lines provided, write the root word for each of the words below.

1. mythical _____
2. official _____
3. discouraging _____
4. equality _____
5. systematic _____
6. indefinite _____

7. measurement _____
8. mysterious _____
9. healthier _____
10. involvement _____
11. uncertainty _____
12. separation _____

7 **Using Words with Many Syllables.** Fill in the blanks in these sentences with the words listed below. Use each word only once.

delirious	fortunate	interference	supervisor
detergent	headquarters	irregular	temperature

1. Bernice's _____ was very high when she had the flu.

2. The official penalized the team for pass _____.

3. Last week, Miguel was promoted to _____ of his section.

4. I can't do a wash until I get some more laundry _____.

5. The doctor discovered an _____ heartbeat during Ted's physical exam.

6. Wanda was _____ with joy when she won the lottery.

7. Winning was the most _____ thing that had ever happened to her.

8. The Simons' house has become the _____ for the neighborhood improvement campaign.

Use two of the listed words in sentences of your own.

_____

_____

8 **Syllable Types.** The six types of syllables you have studied so far are listed below. Write an example of each type of syllable on the lines provided.

Syllable Type	Your Example	Syllable Type	Your Example
1. Closed	_____	4. **VCe**	_____
2. Open	_____	5. Double Vowel	_____
3. Cle	_____	6. R-Controlled	_____

9 **Writing Words by Syllables.** Write the words your teacher dictates by syllables. Then write the entire word on the line provided.

	First Syllable	Second Syllable	Third Syllable	Fourth Syllable	Whole Word
1.	_____	_____			_____
2.	_____	_____			_____
3.	_____	_____			_____
4.	_____	_____	_____		_____
5.	_____	_____	_____		_____
6.	_____	_____	_____		_____
7.	_____	_____	_____		_____
8.	_____	_____	_____	_____	_____
9.	_____	_____	_____	_____	_____
10.	_____	_____	_____	_____	_____

Use four of the words you wrote in original sentences.

_____

_____

_____

_____

10 **Homonyms.** Use each of the homonyms below in an original sentence. Look up their meanings in your dictionary if necessary.

1. led _____

2. lead _____

3. red _____

4. read _____

5. bred _____

6. bread _____

11 **Writing Words That End in Schwa Syllables.** On the lines below, write the words that you hear. All of these words end in /ən/ or /əm/.

1. _____   4. _____   7. _____

2. _____   5. _____   8. _____

3. _____   6. _____   9. _____

12 **Writing Sentences.** On the lines below, write the sentences that you hear.

1. _____

2. _____

3. _____

_____

4. _____

_____

5. _____

_____

13 **Crossword Puzzle.** Use the clues below to complete this crossword puzzle. Most of the answers are family words or sight words from this unit.

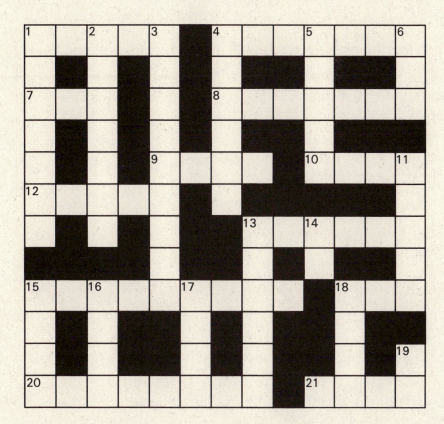

Across

1. What we buy things with
4. Baseball player's concern: batting ___
7. Painting, drawing, or sculpture
8. Hardship; difficulty: He's in a lot of ___.
9. Donate
10. It is on top of your neck.
12. Jewelry worn on fingers
13. Carry on: Can you ___ all by yourself?
15. Decide: The jury will ___ the verdict.
18. A tight bundle: a ___ of money
20. To become liquid; to melt
21. The person who has the leading role in a play

Down

1. Use a ruler to find the length of something
2. Not anything
3. A person who is young
4. Busy, lively, showing action
5. The opposite of smooth
6. A homonym for you
11. Fear; uneasiness: I ___ going to the dentist.
13. Sixty seconds equals one ___.
14. The opposite of yes
15. The opposite of alive
16. These are 2,000 pounds each.
17. The homonym for male
18. To wish for; desire
19. A homonym for oar

Lesson 19

The Word Families *ow*, *owl*, *own*, and *ower*

Occupations			
gardener	athlete	dietician	therapist
mechanic	accountant	receptionist	machinist

Word Families

① Listening

ow

Listen to the sound of *ow* in these words.

now	plow	allow	crowd
vow	towel	drowsy	powder
however	vowel	eyebrow	coward

owl

Listen to the sound of *owl* in these words.

owl	howl	scowl
fowl	growling	prowler

own

Listen to the sound of *own* in these words.

brown	clown	downtown
crown	frown	nightgown

ower

Listen to the sound of *ower* in these words.

power	shower	flower
tower	glowering	sunflower
cower	powerful	cauliflower

② Writing Words. On the lines below, write the words that you hear.

1. _____   4. _____   7. _____

2. _____   5. _____   8. _____

3. _____   6. _____   9. _____

3 Word Building. Write the missing syllable of each word you hear.

1. _____ tet   4. u ni _____   7. war _____

2. re _____ ing   5. re _____   8. af ford a _____

3. Flor i _____   6. _____ phan   9. in _____ ma tion

4 Words That Sound Almost Alike. Below are three pairs of words that sound almost alike. Use each word in an original sentence. Check your dictionary for their meanings if necessary.

1. boor _____

   bore _____

2. moor _____

   more _____

3. poor _____

   pour _____

5 Dictionary Skills: Homonyms. Answer the following questions, using a dictionary when necessary.

1. Is a wild pig a *boar* or a *bore*?   _____

2. Do people get up in the *morning* or in the *mourning*?   _____

3. If you injure a muscle, is it *soar* or *sore*?   _____

4. Do you study for a *coarse* or a *course*?   _____

5. Do you row a boat with an *oar* or an *ore*?   _____

6. Is the number that follows three *four* or *for*?   _____

7. After cheering at a basketball game, are people *hoarse* or *horse*?   _____

8. When people don't have anything to do, are they *board* or *bored*?   _____

9. When you study intently, do you *pore* or *pour* over a book?   _____

10. When you work hard, do you put *forth* or *fourth* an effort?   _____

3 **Writing about Occupations.** Choose one of the occupations listed on the previous page and write a brief job description for it. Include the duties of the position, where the work is performed, and what hours are usually worked.

_____

_____

_____

_____

_____

Now write a brief description of a job you have had or would like to have.

_____

_____

_____

_____

_____

4 **Review of Doubling Patterns 1 and 2.** Add the endings to the words below following Doubling Patterns 1 and 2. Remember that _w_ and _x_ are not doubled.

1. vow + ed _____

2. howl + ing _____

3. hop + ing _____

4. allow + able _____

5. spot + ed _____

6. tower + ing _____

7. crowd + ed _____

8. forgot + en _____

9. propel + er _____

10. clown + ing _____

11. begin + ing _____

12. shower + ed _____

5 **Dictionary Skills: The Two Sounds of *ow*.** The word family *ow* can spell /ō/, as in *know*, and /ou/, as in *now*. The words *bow*, *row*, and *sow* can be pronounced both ways. Look these words up in your dictionary and write a definition for each pronunciation.

1. *bow* as /bou/ _____

2. *bow* as /bō/ _____

3. *row* as /rou/ _____

4. *row* as /rō/ _____

5. *sow* as /sou/ _____

6. *sow* as /sō/ _____

6 **Reviewing Syllable Types**

1. A **closed** syllable ends with a short vowel followed by one or more consonants. Underline the closed syllables below.

   ind   co   ear   ble   ume   ick   or   tain   ap   ove

2. An **open** syllable ends with a vowel that is usually long. Underline the open syllables below.

   ind   co   ear   ble   ume   sti   or   tain   ap   re

3. A **VCe** syllable has a long vowel followed by a consonant and ends with a silent *e*. Underline the **VC**e syllables below.

   ind   co   ear   ble   ume   sti   or   ate   ap   ove

4. A **Cle** syllable has a consonant followed by *le* and usually comes at the end of a word. Underline the Cle syllables below.

   ind   co   ear   ble   ume   ick   or   sle   ap   kle

5. A **double vowel** syllable has two vowels together that make one sound. Underline the double vowel syllables below.

   seap   co   oam   ble   ume   ick   or   tain   ap   pone

6. An **r-controlled** syllable has one or two vowels followed by an *r*. Underline the r-controlled syllables below.

   seap   co   ear   ble   ume   ick   or   tain   ap   ur

7 **Writing Words by Syllables.** Write the words your teacher dictates by syllables. Then write the entire word on the line provided.

First Syllable	Second Syllable	Third Syllable	Fourth Syllable	Whole Word
1. _____	_____	_____		_____
2. _____	_____	_____		_____
3. _____	_____	_____		_____
4. _____	_____	_____		_____
5. _____	_____	_____		_____
6. _____	_____	_____		_____
7. _____	_____	_____		_____
8. _____	_____	_____	_____	_____

Use two of the words you wrote in original sentences.

_____

_____

8 **Writing Sentences.** On the lines below, write the sentences that you hear.

1. _____

2. _____

3. _____

4. _____

_____

5. _____

6. _____

Lesson 20

The Word Families *ou*, *out*, *our*, and *ouch*

	Sight Words	
doubt	drought	counterfeit

Word Families

ou

① Listening

Listen to the sound of *ou* in these words.

loud	noun	foul	bough
cloud	council	gouge	mouth
proud	counselor	thousand	south

out

Listen to the sound of *out* in these words.

out	pout	scout	outcome
bout	spout	shout	outside
about	sprouting	stout	outrageous

our

Listen to the sound of *our* in these words.

our	hour	sour	flour
ourselves	hourly	scour	devour

ouch

Listen to the sound of *ouch* in these words.

ouch	couch	vouch	grouchy
pouch	crouched	voucher	slouching

② Writing Words. On the lines below, write the words that you hear.

1. _____   4. _____   7. _____

2. _____   5. _____   8. _____

3. _____   6. _____   9. _____

3 **Word Building.** Add one of the word families listed below to each of the consonants or blends to make a word. Do not make the same word twice.

ow	*own*	*out*	*ouch*
owl	*ower*	*our*	

1. b_____   4. d_____   7. h_____   10. p_____

2. c_____   5. f_____   8. n_____   11. sc_____

3. c_____   6. h_____   9. p_____   12. sc_____

4 **Compound Words with *Out*.** Form compound words by adding *out* to the beginning or end of each of the words below. Check your dictionary to see if your compounds are closed, hyphenated, or open.

1. doors _____   7. work _____

2. check _____   8. weigh _____

3. live _____   9. cook _____

4. worn _____   10. going _____

5. right _____   11. black _____

6. turn _____   12. through _____

5 **Discovering a Pattern.** You have learned two common spellings for the sound /ou/: *ou* and *ow*. Underline the *ou* or *ow* in the words below and answer the questions that follow.

now	towel	clown	hour	loud	house
plow	power	crowd	amount	mouth	compound

1. Which spelling of /ou/ occurs both in the middle and at the end of words and syllables?

_____

2. Which spelling of /ou/ does not occur at the end of words and syllables? _____

  Pattern: At the end of words and syllables, the sound /ou/ is usually

   spelled _____.

6 Alternative Spellings for /ou/. The sound /ou/ is commonly spelled *ou* and *ow*. If the words or phrases your teacher dictates contain *ou*, write them in the **ou** column. Write them in the **ow** column if they contain *ow*.

ou	ow
_____	_____
_____	_____
_____	_____
_____	_____
_____	_____

7 Alternative Sounds for *Our*. You have learned that *our* spells four different sounds: /ûr/ as in *journey*, /ôr/ as in *four*, /o͝or/ as in *tour*, and /our/ as in *sour*. Write each word below under the appropriate heading.

adjourn	detour	mourn	resource
contour	encourage	ourselves	scouring
courtesy	hourly	pour	tourist

/ûr/ as in *journey*

_____

_____

_____

/ôr/ as in *four*

_____

_____

_____

/o͝or/ as in *tour*

_____

_____

_____

/our/ as in *sour*

_____

_____

_____

8 **Dictionary Skills: Homonyms.** Five pairs of homonyms are listed below. Use each word in an original sentence. Look up the meanings of the words in your dictionary if necessary.

1. our _____

2. hour _____

3. foul _____

4. fowl _____

5. bough _____

6. bow _____

7. council _____

8. counsel _____

9. flour _____

10. flower _____

9 **Writing Sentences.** On the lines below, write the sentences that you hear.

1. _____

2. _____

3. _____
_____

4. _____
_____

5. _____
_____

Lesson 21

The Word Families *ound*, *ount*, *ouse*, and *ounce*

Sight Words

patience	anxious
conscience	anxiety

Word Families

ound

ount

ouse

ounce

1 Listening

Listen to the sound of *ound* in these words.

found	mound	background
sound	pound	compound
round	boundary	confounded
around	astounding	surrounded

Listen to the sound of *ount* in these words.

count	amount	bounty	countdown
county	surmount	fountain	counteract
account	discount	mountaintop	counterclockwise

Listen to the sound of *ouse* in these words.

house	blouse	warehouse	arouse
mouse	spouse	household	trousers

Listen to the sound of *ounce* in these words.

ounce	pounce	trounce	announce
bounce	pronounce	renounce	announcement

2 Writing Words. On the lines below, write the words that you hear.

1. _____   5. _____   9. _____

2. _____   6. _____   10. _____

3. _____   7. _____   11. _____

4. _____   8. _____   12. _____

3 Dictionary Skills: Alphabetizing. On the lines below, alphabetize the words you wrote in Exercise 2.

1. _____   5. _____   9. _____

2. _____   6. _____   10. _____

3. _____   7. _____   11. _____

4. _____   8. _____   12. _____

4 Compound Words with *House* and *Counter*. Form compound words by adding *house* or *counter* to the beginning or the end of the words below.

1. work _____   7. green _____

2. light _____   8. measures _____

3. weight _____   9. attack _____

4. boarding _____   10. fire _____

5. sign _____   11. boat _____

6. part _____   12. keeper _____

5 Homonyms: *Patience* and *Patients*. Write one or two original sentences using the words *patience* and *patients*.

_____

_____

6 **Word Building.** Fill in the blanks in the words below with either *ow* or *ou* to correctly spell words with the /ou/ sound.

1. We f_____nd nine soaking wet t_____els in the sh_____er stalls.

2. H_____ do you pron_____nce the v_____els in that word?

3. A cr_____d gathered _____tside the wareh_____se to watch the blazing fire.

4. The gardener f_____nd a pr_____ler cr_____ching d_____n behind the h_____se.

5. Howard is going to buy some tr_____sers at the new disc_____nt store
   d_____nt_____n.

6. The t_____n c_____ncil voted to spend a th_____sand dollars to repair the
   f_____ntain.

7. The ann_____ncement was made ab_____t an h_____r after we arrived at the
   c_____rth_____se.

8. _____r apartment h_____se is surr_____nded by fl_____ers, but we're not
   all_____ed to pick them.

7 **Review of Silent *e* Patterns 1 and 2.** Add the endings to the words
below following Silent *e* Patterns 1 and 2.

1. house + ing   _____   7. bounce + y   _____

2. pounce + ed   _____   8. douse + ed   _____

3. rescue + er   _____   9. rouse + ing   _____

4. outrage + ous _____   10. espouse + al   _____

5. lounge + ing   _____   11. pronounce + ment _____

6. renounce + ed _____   12. pronounce + able _____

Use two of the words you formed in original sentences.

_____

_____

8 **Proofreading.** It is sometimes hard to know whether to use *ou* or *ow* to spell /ou/. Each of the words below is spelled two ways. Underline the one that you think is correct. Then look up the word in your dictionary to be sure you are right. When you have checked the spelling, write the word on the line provided.

1. bowntiful   bountiful   _____

2. eyebrow   eyebrou   _____

3. renownce   renounce   _____

4. accowntable   accountable   _____

5. scowling   scouling   _____

6. fowndation   foundation   _____

7. cauliflower   cauliflour   _____

8. rowsing   rousing   _____

9. encownter   encounter   _____

10. allowance   allouance   _____

9 **Writing Sentences.** On the lines below, write the sentences that you hear.

1. _____

2. _____

3. _____

4. _____

5. _____

_____

6. _____

_____

Lesson 22

The Word Families *all*, *aw*, *awn*, *awl*, and *awk*

```
                    Sight Words
        guess    guide    Celsius
        guest             Fahrenheit
```

Word Families

① Listening

all

Listen to the sound of *all* in these words.

all	hall	appall	squall
ball	tall	recall	baseball
caller	wall	enthrall	nightfall
fallen	small	overalls	installment

aw

Listen to the sound of *aw* in these words.

saw	claw	thaw	awful
paw	flaw	straw	awesome
raw	lawyer	drawback	jawline

awn

Listen to the sound of *awn* in these words.

dawn	pawn	drawn	awning
lawn	yawn	brawny	

awl

Listen to the sound of *awl* in these words.

awl	brawl	drawl	scrawl
bawl	crawling	shawl	sprawl

awk

Listen to the sound of *awk* in these words.

| hawk | squawk | gawky | awkward |

2 **Writing Words.** On the lines below, write the words that you hear.

1. _____ 5. _____ 9. _____

2. _____ 6. _____ 10. _____

3. _____ 7. _____ 11. _____

4. _____ 8. _____ 12. _____

3 **Using Sight Words.** The terms *Celsius* and *Fahrenheit* refer to different scales for measuring temperature. Use your dictionary to answer the following questions.

1. Where does the term *Celsius* come from? _____
_____

2. Where does the term *Fahrenheit* come from? _____
_____

3. On which scale does water freeze at 32° and boil at 212°? _____

4. On which scale does water freeze at 0° and boil at 100°? _____

5. *Centigrade* is another name for which temperature scale? _____

4 **Alternative Spellings: *all* and *awl*.** Words that end in *all* sound like words that end in *awl*. If the words or phrases your teacher dictates contain *all*, write them in the **all** column. Write them in the **awl** column if they contain *awl*.

all	awl
_____	_____
_____	_____
_____	_____
_____	_____

5 **Writing Words by Syllables.** Write the words your teacher dictates by syllables. Then write the entire word on the line provided.

First Syllable	Second Syllable	Third Syllable	Fourth Syllable	Whole Word
1. _____	_____			_____
2. _____	_____	_____		_____
3. _____	_____	_____		_____
4. _____	_____	_____		_____
5. _____	_____	_____		_____
6. _____	_____	_____		_____
7. _____	_____	_____	_____	_____
8. _____	_____	_____	_____	_____

Use two of the words you wrote in original sentences.

_____

_____

6 **Compound Words with *Ball* and *Fall*.** Build compound words by adding *ball* or *fall* to the beginning or the end of the words below. Use your dictionary to determine whether your compounds are closed, hyphenated, or open.

1. rain _____
2. foot _____
3. water _____
4. room _____
5. pit _____
6. bearing _____

7. wind _____
8. out _____
9. park _____
10. snow _____
11. down _____
12. volley _____

7 **Writing Sentences.** On the lines below, write the sentences that you hear.

1. _____

2. _____

3. _____

4. _____

   _____

5. _____

8 **Composing Sentences.** On a separate sheet of paper, write a paragraph of four or five sentences that describes the scene below.

Lesson 23

The Word Families *al*, *alt*, *au*, *auCe*, *aught*, and *ought*

	Sight Words
exhaust	leopard
somersault	mosquito

Word Families

1 **Listening**

al

Listen to the sound of *al* in these words.

also	already	bald	false
almost	although	scald	walnut

alt

Listen to the sound of *alt* in these words.

salt	exalt	altar	alterations
halt	asphalt	alter	alternatives
malt	falter	alternate	

au

Listen to the sound of *au* in these words.

author	vault	haul	faucet
auction	faulty	haunt	caution
automobile	assault	laundry	defraud

auCe

Listen to the sound of *auCe* in these words.

cause	clause	pause	sauce
because	applause	gauze	saucepan

aught

Listen to the sound of *aught* in these words.

caught	taught	daughter	naughty

ought

Listen to the sound of *ought* in these words.

ought	bought	fought	thought
sought	brought	wrought	thoughtful

2 Writing Words. On the lines below, write the words that you hear.

1. _____   5. _____   9. _____

2. _____   6. _____   10. _____

3. _____   7. _____   11. _____

4. _____   8. _____   12. _____

3 Alternative Spellings: *alt* and *ault*. The spellings *alt* and *ault* are pronounced alike. If the words or phrases your teacher dictates contain *alt*, write them in the **alt** column. Write them in the **ault** column if they contain *ault*.

alt	**ault**
_____	_____
_____	_____
_____	_____
_____	_____
_____	_____

4 Dictionary Skills: Homonyms. Answer the following questions, using a dictionary if necessary.

1. Does a dog have *pause* or *paws*? _____

2. Is a sharp, pointed tool an *all* or an *awl*? _____

3. Does a tiger have *clause* or *claws*? _____

4. Is a passageway in a building a *hall* or a *haul*? _____

5. If a rope is pulled tight, is it *taught* or *taut*? _____

6. If you change something, do you *altar* it or *alter* it? _____

7. If a baby cries loudly, does he *ball* or *bawl*? _____

8. Is a large, heavy hammer a *mall* or a *maul*? _____

5 Proofreading. It is sometimes hard to know which spelling to use when you hear the sound /ô/. Each of the words below is spelled two ways. Underline the one that you think is correct. Then look up the word in your dictionary to be sure you are right. When you have checked the spelling, write the word on the line provided.

1. already	allready	_____
2. haulter	halter	_____
3. cawseway	causeway	_____
4. alright	all right	_____
5. brawny	brauny	_____
6. awsome	awesome	_____
7. somersault	summersault	_____
8. sprauling	sprawling	_____
9. naughty	noughty	_____
10. appalling	appaling	_____

6 Dictionary Skills: Alternative Spellings for /ôt/. The sound /ôt/ can be spelled *aught* or *ought*. Each of the words spelled phonetically below contains the sound /ôt/. Use the dictionary to find the correct spelling based on the definition given. Write the correct spellings on the lines provided.

Phonetic Spelling	Definition	Correct Spelling
1. /ôt/	zero; a cipher	_____
2. /ŏn´slôt/	a violent attack	_____
3. /fôr´thôt/	planning or preparation ahead of time	_____
4. /dĭs trôt´/	anxious or agitated	_____
5. /ō´vər rôt/	nervous or excited	_____

7 **Puzzle.** Use the clues below to fill in the blocks of the puzzle. All of the answer words contain *au*. Use your dictionary if you need to. When you have filled in all of the correct answers, the letters in the shaded blocks will spell a new *au* word.

Clues

1. To show approval by clapping hands

2. The eighth month

3. A person who wrote something

4. To pull with force or to drag something

5. A spigot from which water comes

6. An extinct reptile that lived millions of years ago

7. The season that follows summer

8. A group of people watching a performance

9. To make something happen

The new word: _____

Use the new word in an original sentence.

_____

8 **Writing Sentences.** On the lines below, write the sentences that you hear.

1. _____

2. _____

3. _____

4. _____

5. _____

6. _____

Lesson 24

The Word Families *og*, *off*, *oss*, *ost*, and *oth*

```
┌─────────────────────────────────────────┐
│              Sight Words                 │
│       honk     loft     synagogue        │
└─────────────────────────────────────────┘
```

Word Families

1 Listening

og

Listen to the sound of *og* in these words.

dog	hog	log	dialog
dogmatic	hogwash	logger	catalog

off

Listen to the sound of *off* in these words.

off	offset	coffee	scoff
offer	offhand	toffee	coffin
office	offspring		

oss

Listen to the sound of *oss* in these words.

boss	cross	moss
loss	across	floss
toss	crisscross	glossy

ost

Listen to the sound of *ost* in these words.

cost	lost	frost	accost
costly	foster	defrost	ostrich

oth

Listen to the sound of *oth* in these words.

moth	froth	cloth
broth	betroth	tablecloth

2 **Writing Words.** On the lines below, write the words that you hear.

1. _____   5. _____   9. _____

2. _____   6. _____   10. _____

3. _____   7. _____   11. _____

4. _____   8. _____   12. _____

3 **Compound Words with *Cross* and *Off*.** Form compound words by adding either *cross* or *off* to the beginning or end of the words below. Check your dictionary to see if your compounds are closed, hyphenated, or open.

1. road _____   7. wise _____

2. pay _____   8. blast _____

3. word _____   9. piece _____

4. kick _____   10. send _____

5. take _____   11. lay _____

6. limits _____   12. shoot _____

Use one of your compound words in an original sentence.

_____

4 **Alternative Spellings: *ost* and *ossed*.** Words that end in *ost* sound like the past tense of words that end in *oss*. If the words and phrases that your teacher dictates contain *ost*, write them in the **ost** column. Write them in the **ossed** column if they contain *ossed*.

ost	ossed
_____	_____
_____	_____
_____	_____

5 **Review of Doubling Patterns 1 and 2**. Add the prefixes and suffixes to the words below. Double the final consonant when necessary.

1. fog + y   _____

2. poison + ing   _____

3. flaw + ed   _____

4. log + ing   _____

5. patrol + ed   _____

6. catalog + ing   _____

7. un + thaw + ed   _____

8. dog + ed + ly   _____

9. control + er   _____

10. over + power + ing   _____

6 **Review of the Ending -es**. When a word ends in *s*, *x*, *z*, *ch*, or *sh*, add -*es* instead of -*s* to form the plural. Write the plurals of the words below on the lines provided.

1. loss   _____

2. pouch   _____

3. cross   _____

4. cost   _____

5. boss   _____

6. couch   _____

7. toss   _____

8. wash   _____

9. business   _____

10. tablecloth _____

7 **Syllable Types**. The six types of syllables you have studied so far are listed below. An example of each type is given. Write two more examples of each type of syllable on the lines provided.

Syllable Type	Example	Your Examples	
1. Closed	set	_____	_____
2. Open	re	_____	_____
3. Cle	ble	_____	_____
4. VCe	ake	_____	_____
5. Double Vowel	eem	_____	_____
6. R-Controlled	oar	_____	_____

8 **Writing Words by Syllables.** Write the words your teacher dictates by syllables. Then write the entire word on the line provided.

First Syllable	Second Syllable	Third Syllable	Fourth Syllable	Whole Word
1. _____	_____			_____
2. _____	_____			_____
3. _____	_____	_____		_____
4. _____	_____	_____		_____
5. _____	_____	_____		_____
6. _____	_____	_____	_____	_____
7. _____	_____	_____	_____	_____

Now write this five-syllable word.

8. _____ _____ _____ _____ _____ _____

Use one of the words you wrote in an original sentence.

_____

9 **Writing Sentences.** On the lines below, write the sentences that you hear.

1. _____

2. _____

3. _____

4. _____

5. _____

6. _____

7. _____

8. _____

Lesson 25

The Word Families *oo*, *u*, *oi*, and *oy*

Sight Words			
choir	turquoise	colonel	plaid

Word Families

1 Listening

oo
as /ŏŏ/

Listen to the sound of *oo* in these words.

book	took	hood	foot
look	mistook	neighborhood	good
cook	shook	stood	wooden
hook	crooked	understood	woolen

u
as /ŏŏ/

Listen to the sound of *u* in these words.

full	push	put	pulley
pull	bush	pudding	bulletin
bull	bushel	butcher	cushion

oi

Listen to the sound of *oi* in these words.

boil	voice	coin	avoid
coil	choice	join	moist
soil	noisy	point	exploit
spoil	poison	appointment	thyroid

oy

Listen to the sound of *oy* in these words.

boy	enjoy	convoy	enjoyable
toy	annoy	destroy	annoyance
loyal	employ	corduroy	employment

2 **Writing Words.** On the lines below, write the words that you hear.

1. _____ 5. _____ 9. _____

2. _____ 6. _____ 10. _____

3. _____ 7. _____ 11. _____

4. _____ 8. _____ 12. _____

3 **Discovering a Pattern.** You have learned two common spellings for the sound /oi/: *oi* and *oy*. Underline *oi* or *oy* in the words below and answer the questions that follow.

boy	annoy	loyal	boil	coin	moist
toy	employ	enjoyment	spoil	point	avoid

1. Which spelling of /oi/ occurs in the middle of words and syllables? _____

2. Which spelling of /oi/ occurs at the end of words and syllables? _____

    Pattern: When the sound /oi/ occurs at the end of words or syllables, it is usually

    spelled _____. When /oi/ occurs in the middle of words or syllables, it

    is usually spelled _____.

4 **Alternative Spellings for /ŏŏ/.** The sound /ŏŏ/ is commonly spelled *oo* or *u*. If the words or phrases your teacher dictates contain *oo*, write them in the **oo** column. Write them in the **u** column if they contain *u*.

        oo   **u**

_____ _____

_____ _____

_____ _____

_____ _____

5 **Root Words.** Write the root word for each of the words below.

1. enjoyable _____   4. adjoining _____

2. avoidance _____   5. disappointment _____

3. moisture _____   6. exploitation _____

Choose one of the words above and use it in an original sentence.

_____

6 **Proofreading.** It is sometimes hard to know which spelling to use when you hear the sound /oi/. Each of the words below is spelled two ways. Underline the one that you think is correct. Then look up the word in your dictionary to be sure you are right. When you have checked the spelling, write the word on the line provided.

1. moist   moyst   _____

2. boyling   boiling   _____

3. enjoiment   enjoyment   _____

4. pointer   poynter   _____

5. loialty   loyalty   _____

6. exploytation exploitation _____

7 **Review of Changing y to i.** When adding an ending to a word that ends in Cy, change the y to i unless the ending begins with i. Do not change the final y if there is a vowel before the y. Build the words below following this pattern.

1. noisy + ly _____   7. bounty + ful _____

2. enjoy + ed _____   8. employ + ee _____

3. bully + ing _____   9. costly + er _____

4. glossy + er _____   10. annoy + ed _____

5. destroy + ing _____ 11. naughty + est _____

6. ready + ness _____   12. un + employ + ed _____

8 **Word Building.** Complete each word below by filling in either *oo*, *u*, *oi*, or *oy*. Then write the entire word on the line provided. Use your dictionary if necessary.

1. m_____sten _____

2. peacef_____l _____

3. r_____alty _____

4. outl_____k _____

5. j_____ous _____

6. b_____llion _____

7. p_____nted _____

8. v_____age _____

9. adulth_____d _____

10. p_____sonous _____

Choose one of the words above and use it in an original sentence.

_____

9 **Compound Words with *Book* and *Foot*.** Form compound words by adding either *book* or *foot* to the beginning or end of each word below. Use your dictionary if necessary.

1. hill _____

2. case _____

3. lights _____

4. text _____

5. note _____

6. mark _____

7. tender _____

8. stool _____

10 **Writing Sentences.** On the lines below, write the sentences that you hear.

1. _____

2. _____

3. _____

4. _____

5. _____

6. _____

Review of Unit 5

Other Vowel Sounds and Spellings

1 **Word Building with *ou* and *ow*.** Write one of the word families below in each blank to make a word. Do not make the same word twice.

ow	own	ou	our	ound	ouse
owl	ower	out	ouch	ount	ounce

1. all_____ed   6. cr_____   11. p_____

2. b_____   7. fl_____   12. p_____ful

3. b_____   8. fl_____   13. pr_____ing

4. cl_____d   9. m_____ain   14. sp_____

5. cr_____   10. p_____   15. spr_____

2 **Alternative Spellings for /ou/.** If the words or phrases your teacher dictates contain *ou*, write them in the **ou** column. Write them in the **ow** column if they contain *ow*.

ou	ow
_____	_____
_____	_____
_____	_____
_____	_____

3 **Homonyms with *ou* and *ow*.** Answer the following questions.

1. Is a chicken a *foul* or a *fowl*?   _____

2. Is bread made with *flour* or *flower*?   _____

3. Is a tree limb a *bough* or a *bow*?   _____

4. Will you finish in an *hour* or in an *our*?   _____

5. Is someone who gives advice a *councilor* or a *counselor*?   _____

4 **Word Building with _aw_ and _au_.** Write one of the word families listed below in each of the blanks to make a word. Do not make the same word twice.

aw	awl	al	au	aught
awn	awk	alt	all	ought

1. br_____

2. cr_____

3. d_____er

4. ex_____

5. f_____se

6. h_____

7. h_____

8. l_____ndry

9. l_____yer

10. m_____

11. s_____

12. squ_____

13. t_____

14. th_____

15. y_____

5 **Homonyms with _aw_ and _au_.** Use each of the homonyms below in an original sentence.

1. pause _____

2. claws _____

3. haul _____

4. taught _____

5. alter _____

6 **Writing Words.** Under each spelling below, write four words from the word families in Unit 5 that contain that spelling.

au	aw	ou	ow
_____	_____	_____	_____
_____	_____	_____	_____
_____	_____	_____	_____
_____	_____	_____	_____

7 **Word Building.** Fill in the missing syllable of each word you hear.

1. in _____ ment
2. _____ sel or
3. an _____ ance
4. con _____ ed
5. _____ mat ic

6. em _____ ee
7. cau li _____ er
8. ap _____ ment
9. _____ to mo bile
10. _____ le tin

11. an _____ ment
12. un der _____
13. ta ble _____
14. _____ ter na tive
15. out ra _____

8 **Review of Doubling Patterns 1 and 2.** Build the words indicated below, doubling the final consonant when necessary.

Reminder: When following both doubling patterns, the final consonants *w* and *x* are not doubled.

1. log + ed _____
2. patrol + ing _____
3. thaw + ing _____
4. allow + ance _____

5. dog + ing _____
6. shower + ed _____
7. put + ing _____
8. control + er _____

9 **More Writing Words.** Under each spelling below, write three words from the families in Unit 5 that contain that spelling.

off	oss	ost	oth
_____	_____	_____	_____
_____	_____	_____	_____
_____	_____	_____	_____

oo	u	oi	oy
_____	_____	_____	_____
_____	_____	_____	_____
_____	_____	_____	_____

10 Compound Words

Part A. Form compound words by adding *counter*, *cross*, *fall*, *house*, *off*, or *out* to the beginning or end of the words below. Use your dictionary if necessary.

1. word _____
2. rain _____
3. black _____
4. send _____
5. hand _____
6. light _____

7. part _____
8. keeper _____
9. spring _____
10. water _____
11. doors _____
12. road _____

Part B. Form compound words by adding any word to the beginning or end of the words below. Use your dictionary if necessary.

1. all _____
2. round _____
3. law _____
4. how _____
5. good _____
6. court _____

7. book _____
8. ball _____
9. hound _____
10. salt _____
11. counter _____
12. look _____

11 More Word Building.

Match a syllable from Column 2 with each syllable in Column 1 to make a word. Write the words on the lines provided. Use each syllable in Column 1 only once.

Column 1

a
al
an
aw
bush
dis
fau
flow

Column 2

cet
count
cross
el
er
ful
noy
ready

1. _____
2. _____
3. _____
4. _____

5. _____
6. _____
7. _____
8. _____

12 **Still More Word Building.** Use the syllables in each group to build words. The number of blanks indicates the number of syllables in each word. Write each word first by syllables. Then write the whole word on the line provided.

ful   er   pow   ly   **Whole Word**

1. _____ _____   _____

2. _____ _____ _____   _____

3. _____ _____ _____ _____   _____

a   ly   stound   ing

1. _____ _____   _____

2. _____ _____ _____   _____

3. _____ _____ _____ _____   _____

ous   rage   ly   out

1. _____ _____   _____

2. _____ _____ _____   _____

3. _____ _____ _____ _____   _____

13 **Writing Sentences.** On the lines below, write the sentences that you hear.

1. _____

2. _____

3. _____

4. _____

5. _____

6. _____

7. _____

8. _____

14 **Crossword Puzzle.** Use the clues below to complete this crossword puzzle. Most of the answers are word family or sight words from Unit 5.

Across

1. Let; permit
4. Many people's favorite sport
8. What you dry yourself with
9. A nut-bearing tree
11. The opposite of found
13. A homonym for dew
14. To run again
17. To make public; proclaim
20. A hollow tube used for drinking
22. Cooked ahead of time
25. Helpful; having a use
26. The opposite of yes
28. A job; work: an ___ office
29. Uncooked

Down

1. A person who writes things
2. Someone who practices law

3. "Mirror, mirror, on the ___"
4. The person you work for
5. The past tense of see
6. Having no hair
7. The opposite of big
10. The name of a person, place, or thing
12. It's in your mouth: Stick out your ___.
15. To chew and swallow food
16. At the present time
18. The opposite of downtown
19. Hint: The detective found a ___.
20. Something poured over food
21. Terrible; frightful
22. The opposite of work
23. A piece of money made of metal
24. Pull or drag; sketch
27. Either: now ___ never

Review of Book 4

Other Vowel Sounds and Spellings

Long u Lessons 1-5	Other Long Vowel Spellings Lessons 6-8	R-Controlled Vowels Lessons 9-14	Other Short Vowel Spellings Lessons 15-18	Other Vowel Sounds and Spellings Lessons 19-25

/ōō/ (rule)
or
/yōō/ (use)
 	
ew
o
oo
oof
ool
oom
oon
oop
oose
oot
ooth
ou
u
uce
ude
ue
uke
ule
ume
une
use
ute
	/ā/: ea
	      ei
	      eigh
	      ey
	/ē/: ei
	      i
	      ie
	      iCe
	/ō/: olk
	      ost
	      ough
	      oul
		/ûr/: ear
		(fur) er
		      ir
		      or
		      our
		      ur
		/ər/: ar
		(dollar)
		/ăr/: arr
		(carry)
		/âr/: ar
		(bear) ear
		/ĕr/: er
		(very) err
		/îr/: er
		(here) ere
		/ôr/: ar
		(or) oar
		      or
		      our
		/är/: ar
		(far)
		/ŏŏr/: our
		(your) ure
			/ŏ/: a
			     oll
			     olve
			/ĕ/: ea
			/ĭ/: age
			     ain
			     ate
			     ive
			     iCe
			     ui
			     y
			/ŭ/: o
			     ou
				/ou/: ou
				(out) ouch
				      ounce
				      ound
				      ount
				      our
				      ouse
				      out
				      ow
				      ower
				      owl
				      own
				/ô/: al
				(all) all
				     alt
				     au
				     aught
				     auCe
				     aw
				     awk
				     awl
				     awn
				     off
				     og
				     oss
				     ost
				     oth
				     ought
				/ŏŏ/: oo
				(book) u
				/oi/: oi
				     oy

1 **Other Vowel Sounds and Spellings.** The chart on the previous page shows the patterns for spelling the vowel sounds presented in this text. Some of these spellings are listed below. Write one word that contains each of these spellings.

/ā/

1. ea _____
2. ei _____
3. eigh _____
4. ey _____

/ē/

1. ei _____
2. i _____
3. ie _____
4. iCe _____

/ō/

1. olk _____
2. ost _____
3. ough _____
4. oul _____

/ōo/

1. o _____
2. ooC _____
3. ou _____
4. u _____
5. uCe _____

/ou/

1. ow _____
2. out _____
3. ound _____
4. ount _____
5. ouse _____

/ô/

1. al _____
2. all _____
3. au _____
4. aw _____
5. ought _____

/ĭ/

1. ain _____
2. ui _____

/ŏ/

1. a _____
2. oll _____

/ŭ/

1. o _____
2. ou _____

/ŏo/

1. oo _____
2. u _____

/oi/

1. oi _____
2. oy _____

/ûr/

1. er _____
2. ur _____

2 **R-Controlled Vowels.** Fill in the missing syllable of each word you hear.

1. _____ son al
2. A _____ i can
3. in te ri _____
4. gov _____ ment
5. trans _____ ent
6. _____ gent ly
7. e _____ gen cy
8. pop u _____
9. con _____ ma tion

3 **Patterns at the End of Words.** The patterns listed below are commonly found at the end of words. Write one word that ends in each of these spellings.

1. aw _____   5. ough _____

2. ew _____   6. ow _____

3. ey _____   7. oy _____

4. oo _____   8. ue _____

4 **Review of Syllable Types.** The six types of syllables you have studied are listed below. Write one example of each type.

Closed _____   Cle _____   Double Vowel _____

Open _____   VCe _____   R-Controlled _____

5 **Writing Words by Syllables.** Write the words your teacher dictates by syllables. Then write the entire word on the line provided.

First Syllable	Second Syllable	Third Syllable	Fourth Syllable	Whole Word
1. _____	_____	_____		_____
2. _____	_____	_____		_____
3. _____	_____	_____		_____
4. _____	_____	_____		_____
5. _____	_____	_____		_____
6. _____	_____	_____		_____
7. _____	_____	_____		_____

Now write this five-syllable word.

8. _____ _____ _____ _____ _____ _____

Use one of the words you wrote in an original sentence.

_____

6 **Word Building.** Add the prefixes and suffixes to the words below. Follow the patterns for adding endings that you have studied.

1. review + ing _____
2. tie + ing _____
3. vary + ous _____
4. annoy + ance _____
5. log + ing _____
6. refer + ing _____
7. notice + ably _____
8. reduce + ing _____
9. swap + ed _____
10. double + ing _____

11. loss + s *or* es _____
12. outrage + ous _____
13. fur + y + er _____
14. yourself + s *or* es _____
15. im + prove + ment _____
16. un + die + ing _____
17. country + s *or* es _____
18. opportune + ity _____
19. substitute + ion _____
20. in + dispute + able _____

7 **Reviewing Homonyms.** Use each of the following homonyms in an original sentence.

1. due _____
2. route _____
3. break _____
4. wear _____
5. soar _____
6. bread _____
7. hour _____
8. piece _____
9. dessert _____
10. cereal _____

8 Proofreading. Each of the words below is spelled two ways. Underline the one that you think is correct. Then look up the word in your dictionary to be sure you are right. When you have checked the spelling, write the word on the line provided.

1. feild	field	_____
2. private	privit	_____
3. cartoon	cartune	_____
4. poisin	poison	_____
5. squall	squawl	_____
6. thay	they	_____
7. caught	cought	_____
8. Tuesday	Tuseday	_____
9. very	verry	_____
10. allready	already	_____

9 Word Building

Part A. Write either *ar*, *er*, or *or* in each blank below to form a word that ends in /ər/.

1. dang_____	4. doll_____	7. mot_____	10. barri_____
2. doct_____	5. garden_____	8. corn_____	11. superi_____
3. moth_____	6. hon_____	9. cell_____	12. regul_____

Part B. Write either *ei* or *ie* in each blank below to form a word that contains long *e*.

1. bel___f	4. ach___ve	7. s___ze	10. bel___ve
2. n___ther	5. c___ling	8. y___ld	11. conc___ve
3. n___ce	6. mov___	9. rec___ve	12. rel___ved

10 Crossword Puzzle. Use the clues below to complete this crossword puzzle. Most of the answers are family words or sight words from Book 4.

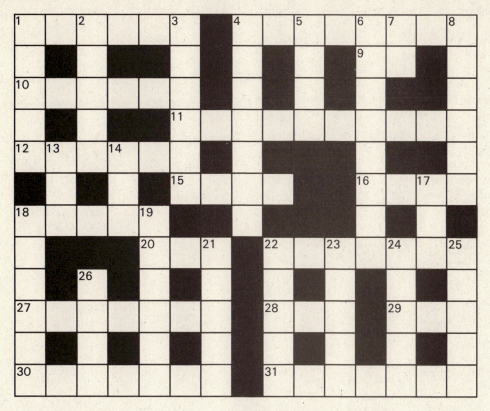

Across

1. The time to come: ___ plans
4. The opposite of northern
9. A homonym for ore
10. A homonym for wait
11. Half the earth: the western ___
12. To save from harm or danger
15. A space enclosed by walls
16. One thing that is part of a whole
18. A homonym for herd
20. Painting, drawing, or sculpture
22. Hot, dry places
27. A meat used on pizza
28. A place to see animals
29. A homonym for ewes
30. Honest, true: a ___ compliment
31. Your brother's sons

Down

1. Not as many; smaller in number
2. Groups of three
3. One or the other: ___ this or that
4. You wash your hair with this.
5. Operates or puts into action
6. A greenhouse; a place where plants are grown
7. A suffix meaning someone who does something
8. Purchased most recently
13. A female sheep
14. An automobile
17. Abbreviation for interest
18. Buildings people live in
19. To injure or harm something
21. A homonym for they're
22. Twelve of something
23. To bend down; a doorstep
24. A homonym for root
25. Cooks meat and vegetables slowly
26. Change direction: ___ right at the next corner.

Word Families and Representative Words

Lesson 1

ude
aptitude
attitude
conclude
crude
delude
denude
gratitude
include
intrude
latitude
longitude
prelude
protrude
rude
seclude
solitude

use
abuse
accuse
amusement
confuse
diffuse
excuse
fuse
misuse
profuse
refuse
use
useful

uce
deduce
inducement
introduce
produce
reduce
reproduce
spruce
truce

ule
capsule
molecule
mule
ridicule
rule
ruler
schedule
yule

Lesson 2

ute
absolute
astute
commute
computer
cute
dilute
dispute
distribute
execute
flute
mute
parachute
pollute
prosecute
salute
substitute

ume
assume
consumer
costume
fume
legume
perfume
plume
presume
resume

une
attuned
communed
dune
immune
June
opportune
prune
tune

uke
duke
fluke
Luke
rebuke

Lesson 3

u
duty
flu
fluent
fuel
future

human
humor
menu
ruby
ruin
rumor
super
truly
union
unit
universe

ue
argue
clue
continue
due
glue
gruesome
issue
pursue
rescue
residue
statue
subdue
sue
Tuesday
true
value

ew
blew
chew
curfew
drew
few
flew
grew
Jewish
nephew
new
renew
steward

o
ado
approval
improve
into
move
movement
prove
remover
tomb

whom
womb
unto

Lesson 4

oo
bamboo
boost
food
moody
noodle
rooster
shampoo
taboo
tattoo
too
woo
zoo

oon
afternoon
balloon
cartoon
cocoon
honeymoon
maroon
moon
noon
raccoon
soon
tablespoon
typhoon

oom
boom
bloom
broomstick
classroom
courtroom
doom
gloom
heirloom
mushroom
room
storeroom
zoom

ool
cool
fool
foolish
footstool
school

spool
tool
whirlpool

oof
aloof
fireproof
foolproof
proof
roof
spoof

Lesson 5

oop
coop
droop
hoop
loophole
scoop
snoop
stoop
troop

oot
boot
hoot
loot
offshoot
root
scooter
shoot
uproot

oose
caboose
choose
goose
loose
loosen
moose
noose

ooth
booth
smooth
soothing
tooth
toothache
toothbrush

ou
coupon
group
rouge

route
routine
soup
you
youth

Lesson 6

ea as /ā/
break
breakdown
daybreak
great
Great Britain
Great Plains
outbreak
steak

ei as /ā/
beige
feint
reign
rein
reindeer
veil
vein

eigh as /ā/
eight
eighth
freight
neighbor
neighborhood
sleigh
weigh
weight

ey as /ā/
convey
hey
prey
obey
survey
they

Lesson 7

ie as /ē/
achievement
belief
believe
brief
calorie
field
grief

movie
niece
piece
prairie
relief
relieve
series
thief
yield

ei as /ē/
caffeine
ceiling
conceive
deceit
either
leisure
neither
perceive
protein
receipt
receive
seize

i as /ē/
chili
exterior
interior
kilo
liter
ski
superior
taxi
trio

iCe as /ēC/
automobile
elite
figurine
gasoline
magazine
marine
petite
police
prestige
quarantine
routine
vaccine

Lesson 8

ough as /ō/
although
borough
dough

doughnut
furlough
thorough
thoroughfare
thoroughly
though

oul as /ōl/
boulder
poultry
shoulder
soul
soulful

ost as /ōst/
almost
foremost
ghost
guidepost
host
innermost
most
mostly
post
postage
poster
postpone

olk as /ōk/
folklore
folks
folk song
polka
polka dot
yolk

Lesson 9
er as /ûr/
allergy
concert
desert
dessert
determined
emergency
exert
fertile
hers
interpret
nervous
permanent
remember
service
term
vertical

ir as /ûr/
affirm

bird
birth
circle
circus
confirm
firm
flirt
infirmary
irk
quirk
shirk
sir
smirk
squirt
stir

ur as /ûr/
blur
burnt
current
curve
fur
furnish
hurt
injury
occur
purchase
return
spur
suburb
surgery
urban
urgent

Lesson 10
or as /ûr/
and /ər/
error
doctor
favorite
flavor
honor
mirror
word
work
world
worry
worst
worth

our as /ûr/
adjourn
courage
courtesy
discourage
encouragement
flourish

journal
journey
nourish

ear as /ûr/
earl
early
earnest
earth
heard
rehearse
research
search

ar as /ər/
awkward
backwards
blizzard
cellar
circular
collar
dollar
forward
hazard
mustard
popular
regular

Lesson 11
arr as /ăr/
arrogant
arrow
barrel
barren
barrier
carriage
carrot
carry
embarrass
marriage
marry
narration
narrator
narrow
parrot

ar as /âr/
hilarious
humanitarian
librarian
parent
precarious
scarcity
transparent
variation
vary

vegetarian
vicarious
wary

ear as /âr/
bear
bearer
overbearing
pear
swear
tear
underwear
wear

Lesson 12
er as /ĕr/
American
ceremony
cherish
clerical
geriatric
heritage
merit
peril
perishable
serenade
sheriff
stereo
sterilize
therapy
verify
very

err as /ĕr/
cherry
derrick
errand
error
ferris wheel
herring
raspberry
serrated
terrace
terrified
territory
terror

er as /îr/
bacteria
cafeteria
cereal
deteriorate
experience
exterior
hero
inferior
material

mysterious
period
serial
series
serious
superior
zero

ere as /îr/
adhere
atmosphere
hemisphere
here
interfere
merely
severe
sincere
sphere

Lesson 13
or as /ôr/
born
corner
florist
former
glory
historian
horn
inventory
mandatory
order
ordinary
organ
organize
pictorial
story
victorious

oar as /ôr/
aboard
boar
hoard
hoarse
oar
roar
soar
uproar

our as /ôr/
courthouse
courtship
fourth
gourd
mourn
pour
recourse
resourceful

ar as /ôr/
quarrel
quart
quarter
reward
swarm
swarthy
thwart
war
ward
warm
warning
warrant

Lesson 14
ar as /är/
architect
arctic
arm
art
bark
card
charm
depart
far
hardly
jar
mar
mark
partner
party
star

ure as /yŏŏr/
or /ŏŏr/
assure
cure
endure
figure
insure
lure
mature
obscure
procedure
pure
secure
sure

our as /ŏŏr/
contour
courier
detour
gourmet
tour
tourist
your
yourself

Lesson 15
a as /ŏ/
equality
qualify
quality
quantity
squabble
swallow
swamp
swap
wad
waddle
wallet
wan
wander
want
wasp
watch

oll as /ŏl/
college
collie
doll
dollar
follow
Holland
holler
hollow
jolly
pollen
trolley
volley

olve as /ŏlv/
dissolve
involve
resolve
revolve
solve

ea as /ĕ/
bread
breath
dead
death
dread
feather
head
health
instead
measure
pleasure
ready
spread
sweater
thread
weather

Lesson 16

age as /ĭj/
advantage
average
baggage
beverage
cabbage
damage
discourage
encourage
heritage
image
manage
message
mileage
mortgage
package
village

ate as /ŭt/
accurate
adequate
appropriate
climate
considerate
deliberate
delicate
fortunate
moderate
private
separate
ultimate

ive as /ĭv/
active
adjective
captive
festive
fugitive
give
incentive
live
motive
native
negative
olive
pensive
positive
talkative
tentative

iCe as /ĭC/
definite
determine
examine
exquisite
famine
genuine
infinite
justice
notice
office
practice
respite

Lesson 17

y as /ĭ/
bicycle
gym
hymn
mysterious
myth
physical
rhythm
syllable
symbol
sympathy
symphony
symptom
synagogue
synonym
system
typical

ain as /ĭn/
bargain
captain
certain
chaplain
chieftain
curtain
fountain
mountain

ui as /ĭ/
biscuit
build
building
built
circuit
guilt
guilty
guitar

Lesson 18

o as /ŭ/
above
among
another
become
brother
discovery
dozen
front
govern
money
month
nothing
other
oven
shovel
son
stomach
ton
tongue
wonder

ou as /ŭ/
country
couple
cousin
double
enough
rough
southern
touch
tough
trouble
young
youngster

Lesson 19

ow
allow
coward
crowd
drowsy
eyebrow
however
now
plow
powder
towel
vow
vowel

owl
fowl
growling
howl
owl
prowler
scowl

own
brown
clown
crown
downtown
frown
nightgown

ower
cauliflower
cower
flower
glowering
power
powerful
shower
sunflower
tower

Lesson 20

ou
bough
cloud
council
counselor
foul
gouge
loud
mouth
noun
proud
south
thousand

out
about
bout
out
outcome
outrageous
outside
pout
scout
shout
spout
sprouting
stout

our
devour
flour
hour
hourly
our
ourselves
scour
sour

ouch
couch
crouched
grouchy
ouch
pouch
slouching
vouch
voucher

Lesson 21

ound
around
astounding
background
boundary
compound
confounded
found
mound
pound
round
sound
surrounded

ount
account
amount
bounty
count
countdown
counteract
counterclockwise
county
discount
fountain
mountaintop
surmount

ouse
arouse
blouse
house
household
mouse
spouse
trousers
warehouse

ounce
announce
announcement
bounce
ounce
pounce
pronounce
renounce
trounce

Lesson 22

all
all
appall
ball
baseball
caller
enthrall
fallen
hall
installment
nightfall
overalls
recall
small
squall
tall
wall

aw
awesome
awful
claw
drawback
flaw
jawline
lawyer
paw
raw
saw
straw
thaw

awn
awning
brawny
dawn
drawn
lawn
pawn
yawn

awl
awl
bawl
brawl
crawling
drawl
scrawl
shawl
sprawl

awk
awkward
gawky
hawk
squawk

Lesson 23

al
almost
already
also
although
bald
false
scald
walnut

alt
altar
alter
alterations
alternate
alternatives
asphalt
exalt
falter
halt
malt
salt

au
assault
auction
author
automobile
caution
defraud
faucet
faulty
haul
haunt
laundry
vault

auCe
applause
because
cause
clause
gauze
pause
sauce
saucepan

aught
caught
daughter
naughty
taught

ought
bought
brought
fought
ought
sought
thought

thoughtful
wrought

Lesson 24

og
catalog
dialog
dog
dogmatic
hog
hogwash
log
logger

off
coffee
coffin
off
offer
offhand
office
offset
offspring
scoff
toffee

oss
across
boss
crisscross
cross
floss
glossy
loss
moss
toss

ost
accost
cost
costly
defrost
foster
frost
lost
ostrich

oth
betroth
broth
cloth
froth
moth
tablecloth

Lesson 25

oo as /o͝o/
book
cook
crooked
foot
good
hood
hook
look
mistook
neighborhood
shook
stood
took
understood
wooden
woolen

u as /o͝o/
bull
bulletin
bush
bushel
butcher
cushion
full
pudding
pull
pulley
push
put

oi
appointment
avoid
boil
choice
coil
coin
exploit
join
moist
noisy
point
poison
soil
spoil
thyroid
voice

oy
annoy
annoyance

boy
convoy
corduroy
destroy
employ
employment
enjoy
enjoyable
loyal
toy

Sight Words and Thematic Words

Word	Lesson Number	Word	Lesson Number	Word	Lesson Number
accountant	19	geyser	4	prescription	9
Africa	1	gourmet	6	privilege	16
amateur	14	grandeur	14	pursuit	3
ambulance	9	groceries	17	pyramid	12
Antarctica	1	gross	8	receptionist	19
antique	7	guess	22	recipe	17
anxiety	21	guest	22	recruit	3
anxious	21	guide	22	rubella	11
appendicitis	11	guy	4	sabotage	15
arthritis	11	handkerchief	16	sausage	18
Asia	1	hearth	14	sauté	6
athlete	19	hearty	14	seizure	10
aura	13	heir	12	sew	8
Australia	1	hepatitis	11	sieve	16
bacteria	10	honk	24	somersault	23
ballet	6	hospital	9	sorrow	14
beau	8	hygiene	10	sorry	14
bologna	18	infection	10	soufflé	5
boor	13	intrigue	7	South America	1
bouillon	5	irritate	12	souvenir	5
bouquet	5	leopard	23	spinach	17
broccoli	17	loft	24	squash	17
buffet	6	London	2	suave	15
bureau	8	lyric	12	synagogue	24
business	16	machinist	19	syrup	18
café	6	maneuver	3	tableau	8
camouflage	15	margarine	18	technique	7
Celsius	22	mechanic	19	therapist	19
choir	25	Mexico City	2	tier	12
colonel	25	minute	16	Tokyo	2
conscience	21	mischief	16	tonsillitis	11
control	8	moor	13	troupe	5
corsage	15	Moscow	2	turquoise	25
counterfeit	20	mosquito	23	tyranny	12
crochet	6	muscle	4	unique	7
cuckoo	4	neuter	3	vegetables	17
dietician	19	neutral	3	virus	10
dinosaur	13	North America	1	wash	4
doubt	20	nuisance	3	Washington, D.C.	2
drought	20	Ottawa	2	water	4
Europe	1	patience	21	weird	12
ewe	3	patient	9	yogurt	18
exhaust	23	patrol	8		
Fahrenheit	22	pharmacy	9		
fatigue	7	pier	12		
feud	3	pizza	18		
fiancé	6	plaid	25		
fiancée	6	plateau	8		
garage	15	pneumonia	11		
gardener	19	poison	10		

My Personal Word List

Glossary of Terms

affix   A word element that carries meaning and is attached to a root word. Prefixes and suffixes are affixes; for example, *de-* and *-ful* in *delightful*.

blend   The joining together of two or more sounds with each sound still being heard; for example. /tr/ in *trade*.

C   A symbol representing any consonant.

compound word   A word formed by combining two or more words. Compound words can be closed (*greenhouse*), hyphenated (*red-letter*), or open (*yellow jacket*).

diacritical mark   A mark added to a letter to show how to pronounce the letter; for example, the straight line over a vowel to show a long vowel sound.

digraph   A pair of letters that represents one sound; for example, *ch* making the sound /ch/ in *chain* and *ea* making the sound /ē/ in *sea*.

family   A letter pattern or sequence such as *ine* in *fine, mine*, and *combine*. The pattern usually forms a common syllable ending and is composed of a vowel or vowel combination plus the consonant(s) that go with it.

homonym   One of a pair or more of words having the same sound but different meanings and often different spellings; for example, *tail* and *tale*.

pattern   A recurrent, usually predictable sequence of letters. Patterns occur in common syllables (e.g., *ope*) as well as in prefixes, suffixes, roots, and compound words. Spelling rules also produce patterns.

prefix   A word element that carries meaning and is attached to the beginning of a root word; for example, *pre-* in *prepaid*.

schwa   A vowel sound that usually occurs in unstressed syllables in English as heard in the first syllable of *against*; also the symbol (ə) often used to represent the sound.

sight word   A word that is not phonetically predictable; also any word for which students have not had the phonics to enable them to spell the word phonetically.

suffix   A word element that carries meaning and is attached to the end of a root word; for example, *-less* in *speechless*.

syllable   A spoken unit of uninterrupted sound containing one vowel sound producing either a word (e.g., *pay*) or a distinct part of a word (e.g., *pay* or *ment* in *payment*); the letters producing that sound in the word.

V   A symbol representing any vowel.

Style Notes

/x/ A letter between slashes indicates a sound rather than a spelling; for instance, /b/ is the sound produced by the letter *b*.

/ă/ A curved mark (breve) over a vowel indicates the short vowel sound.

/ā/ A straight line (macron) over a vowel indicates the long vowel sound.

/â/ This mark (circumflex) is often used to indicate the vowel sound in r-controlled syllables.

/ä/ This mark (dieresis) indicates the sound of *a* in *far*.

/ə/ This indicates the schwa sound.